Construction Knowledge

By Charlie Scott

Everything You Need To Know About Choosing A Builder And Building Your New Home

For information contact:

Charlie Scott
The Estridge Companies
Carmel, Indiana
www.estridge.com

ISBN 0-9760012-0-9

Written, edited and designed in the USA
Printed in China

DEDICATION

To my lovely wife Sara and our children, Charlie and Ashley, all of whom have (I hope) forgiven me for the hundreds of hours of family time spent researching, writing, rewriting, editing, rewriting, editing, editing, and editing this book. I couldn't have done it without your love, understanding, and support.

Also, to all those employees of The Estridge Companies, both present and past, who live by our common vision to "serve and enrich the lives of others." And, last but not least, to Paul E. Estridge Jr. for creating a company that serves people, (including me,) on both sides of the home's threshold.

ABOUT THE AUTHOR

Charlie Scott is Executive Vice President with The Estridge Companies, one of Indiana's premier residential building companies and winner of several awards, including the 1998 National Housing Quality award.

Through his books and seminars, Charlie has shared his knowledge of new home construction with thousands of homebuyers and real estate professionals and has been a guest speaker/presenter nationally and internationally. He has presented at the National Association of Home Builders, National Association of Realtors, Indiana University Purdue University in Indianapolis, United Kingdom's Building Homes Conference, and many other home building industry venues.

Charlie is an avid runner, cyclist, duathlete, and hiker. He has run numerous marathons and represented Team USA at the 2003 World Duathlon Championships in Switzerland.

Charlie comes from a family of educators and enjoys carrying on the tradition. He likes to use simple language, analogies, and a lot of pictures to make learning easier, enjoyable and more memorable. His goal is to create "edutainment books," which he describes as a mixture of education and entertainment.

TABLE OF CONTENTS

WHAT PEOPLE ARE SAYING:

"Construction Knowlege 101 is a marvelous resource for anyone interested in the homebuilding process. This book very succinctly communicates both the construction processes and the strategies behind a home builder's value proposition."

Chuck Graham, Newton & Graham Consultants

"Whether you are buying or building your first home or already own a house, reading this book will educate you as to basics of home construction which will help you better understand and preserve the value of one of the most important investments you will make."

Dr. Jeffrey D. Fisher, Ph.D., Dunn Professor of Real Estate, Indiana University

"Our customer satisfaction research work for home builders across the country provides the opportunity to vicariously relive literally thousands of new home buying experiences each year. We find that a little construction knowledge can be a huge help to new home buyers. Making wise choices requires having the right information, and Construction Knowledge 101 is an outstanding place to start. Charlie Scott has done a great job of explaining what can be a very complex product and process."

Keith O'Brien, Woodland, O'Brien & Associates

INTRODUCTION

Did you know that the housing industry is second only to the federal government in its contribution to the United States' economy? Did you know that almost 70% of Americans own their own homes?

Did you know that the vast majority of these 65 million American homeowners don't have a clue as to how a home is built?

Home equity is one of the largest contributors to our population's net worth; yet, our lack of knowledge about how homes are built has cost homeowners billions upon billions of dollars in terms of home maintenance and lost resale value—not to mention a more enjoyable homeownership experience.

I believe that the best defense against poor homeownership decisions is education. Therefore, with the help of dozens of people, I have written *Construction Knowledge 101*. In this book, you'll find answers about the basic construction sequence of a home and the timeframe in which a home should be built. But, most important, you'll learn the questions to ask when it comes to building a new home.

Almost anybody can go to one of the 8,000 lumberyards in the United States to buy the sticks and bricks needed to build a house. But it isn't the sticks and bricks that make a house a home: it is the people, starting with the builder, who put the house together that make the home. This book is going to shed new light on what makes a builder tick. Once you know how (and why) a builder ticks, you'll be adequately armed to make sure you're getting the most

Many builders today use models to demonstrate their homes.

for your housebuying dollar—and that your home will be something you'll come to appreciate both emotionally and financially.

In general, people are very interested in how homes are built. I know this because the most frequently asked question homebuyers have of their builder is, "Why did you do things that way?"

Customers and interested bystanders alike are fascinated by the construction process. It's pretty darned interesting to see a parcel of dirt transformed into a beautiful new home, and building is such a complicated and time-intensive process that everyone wants to know how all the pieces of the puzzle go together.

Inevitably, people encounter things they don't understand. How do you know where to build the home? What's the difference between a panelized home and a stick-built home? Should I have 16"-on-center walls or 24"-on-center walls? What's the difference between a heat pump and a high efficiency gas furnace? Can I make my dining room three feet wider? Why is it that the concrete sidewalk isn't the same color as the concrete driveway?

Well, I've been in the new home construction business since 1987. I started as a salesperson with a very high quality homebuilder, The Estridge Group. I quickly learned that a lot of builders sold their homes much cheaper than we could. So I made it my mission to understand how and why our company built homes differently from our competitors. What I learned, was, to me, shocking. The more I learned about the types of decisions a homebuilder makes for the uneducated buyer, the more concerned I became. There are hundreds of decisions to be made in the homebuilding process and practically all of them involve some cost/benefit analysis. If homebuyers aren't knowledgeable about how and why things get done, they're vulnerable to decisions that are in the best financial interest of the builder—not the buyer.

So, this book has been written as the antidote to the homebuyer's homebuilding ignorance. And I mean ignorance in the politest possible sense. If you're not a builder, you probably just don't know much about building a home.

Let me tell you how this book came about.

When I first became an Estridge salesperson, I came to understand that to be a professional, knowledgeable salesperson and to be able to consult and serve our customers, I first had to learn the basics of home construction myself.

So I did. I took notes. Met with builders. Met with suppliers and laborers. Read product literature. Shopped our competitors' homes and products. Read trade magazines. Attended dozens of seminars. And spoke to as many of the nation's best and most ethical homebuilders as possible to understand how they would build a home they'd want their own children to live in. Most of these resources were readily available right here at The Estridge Group. In fact, many of my fellow salespeople helped in the initial collection of this knowledge. We gathered information from fellow career partners, including Paul Estridge Jr., Randy McNutt, Brad Love, Mike Keller, Gary McNutt, Scott Wentz, Steve Wendt, Jeff Ford, Brandon Reider, Paul Godby, Dave Redlin, Brian Rundle, Jaimie Maple, Mike Walker, Rob McGraw, Brett Conrad and Rickie Todd. I also received a lot of helpful input from Ron Benkert, Patrick Boyle,

Tom Korecki, Tom Shurig, Chuck Graham, Keith O'Brien, Bob Schultz, Scott Sedam, April Sjohom, Judy Roberts, Jill Wilkes, and proofreader extraordinaire Kay Scott.

The more that was collected, the more it seemed appropriate for our customers to know how we built houses—and, more important, why we chose to use certain techniques and products. I quickly learned that there were many, many corners that could be cut (both figuratively and literally) in home construction. And many of these corners were completely hidden from the homebuyer's less-experienced eye. Fortunately, Estridge was and is a builder of very high integrity that builds homes "like those we build for our own families." This "do unto others" philosophy has helped The Estridge Companies grow to become Indiana's premier homebuilder and has brought about numerous national accolades.

So this book wasn't just telling readers how to build a house. It was showing them how one of America's finest, most respected builders built homes.

Almost from the beginning, the book was a big success. The first edition of *Construction Knowledge 101* was a little spiral-bound booklet made on a photocopier. We started using it immediately to educate salespeople. People liked it so much, we expanded the material into a soft-cover second edition, which has been used in real estate agent continuing education courses, as a college-level construction management resource, and as a homebuyer's guide to a smart new home purchase. It grew to truly become an inside look at the construction process that could assist people in choosing the right builder and help them know what to expect every step of the way.

Well, as times change, construction techniques and products change, too.

So the book you're now holding is *Construction Knowledge 101, Third Edition.* I think it's the best, most complete version of the book yet.

Design-Build homes are true custom homes. They are designed from scratch and custom built for the customer .

This book is written by me; however, you'll notice that I use the word "we" throughout the book when offering opinions and advice. This book, just like a home, couldn't be built by one person. It takes hundreds of people—salespeople, project managers, trade partners, purchasing agents, manufacturers, consultants, and others — to build a great home, and each of them has contributed directly or indirectly to the contents of this book. I also worked with Ken Honeywell, who helped me turn our *Construction Knowledge 101* textbook into a more user-friendly, easier read. Ken also has added several callouts and readers' aids to help clarify some of the technical aspects of new home construction. And, finally, Paul Wilson designed and laid out a very aesthetically pleasing book.

I hope you like the results and find the book enjoyable. But mostly, I hope you find the book educational and useful. It is truly my pleasure to be a part of helping you grow your construction knowledge. It is my sincere hope that you benefit from the time that you are investing in protecting and arming yourself with this powerful knowledge.

Charlie Scott
March 2004

CHAPTER ONE

It's time to start doing your homework (literally)

So, you've decided to build a new home. Congratulations! Just about all of us dream of building a new home. You are taking the steps to make your dream a reality.

And, once you make the decision to build, the dreaming is only beginning. Your mind may fill with visions of playing catch with your kids in your beautifully landscaped yard...enjoying coffee and breakfast in your nook as the sun comes up to start the day... cuddling on the couch in front of a warm fire in your family room...chatting with friendly neighbors over the barbecue or on the front porch or while you stroll the neighborhood on a quiet Sunday afternoon.

That's all wonderful. And these visions will all become reality—*as long as you do your homework now.* Turning any dream into reality is hard work, and building a home is no exception. It's such an exciting and heady proposition that it's easy to look past the complexities and potential pitfalls of the process—a process that requires careful thought and planning and a thorough understanding of who does what and what happens when. In other words, whether you're the homeowner, a real estate agent, or the builder yourself, the foundation of all new home construction is knowledge.

Education—gaining that knowledge—is what this book is all about.

From the time you sign the building contract to the time you move in, hundreds of professionals will have participated in the building process: the architect who designs the floor plan, the excavator who clears the lot, the masons, carpet layers, electricians, plumbers, and many, many others. This wide range of professionals uses specialized products and materials that are, in turn, provided by a wide variety of manufacturers. Obviously, you want the best quality products you can afford to go into your new home—just as you want the best people working with those products. As you might imagine—but maybe have not begun to imagine until now—orchestrating these many tradespeople, elements, and details is a daunting and laborious task.

That's why you need to choose a builder who has experience working with the best tradespeople and materials. When it comes to making good choices and creating a workable plan for putting everything together, a skilled, experienced, quality-conscious homebuilder can make all the difference in the world.

And that's only the first place your builder makes a huge difference in the process; in fact, *your selection of a builder is the single most critical decision you will face in making your dream a reality.* Remember: it may be the materials that ultimately make up the house, but it's the people who put the house together using those materials, and the management of the entire building process, that make the house the dream home you really want—as efficiently and hassle-free as possible. It's like the difference between hiring a cook and hiring a chef. Both can feed you. But one's going to do a better, more elegant job of concentrating on both the meal and the experience.

You should also understand that one of the most important people responsible for your new home is you. Which is another reason the builder you choose is so important. If you choose a reputable builder, you can be as involved or uninvolved in the process as you'd care to be. If you choose a less-reputable builder, you're going to have to be involved. Very involved.

We think the best plan is to choose a great builder and stay involved. That often means asking questions—dozens, maybe hundreds of questions before the process is finished. You might actually be seeing your builder as often as your own family members (which is another great reason to choose your builder carefully). As an integral part of your new home construction team, you will play a critical role in communication and decision-making throughout the four to five months it takes to build your home.

Think you're just being a bother? Think again. Any builder you want building your home wouldn't have it any other way. Any builder you want building your home should be more than willing to answer any question you have. Your builder wants you to be a happy customer, and keeping you informed about the process is one more way to ensure that's exactly what happens.

Homebuilding Trends: What's Being Built Today

There's an old adage in the homebuilding industry: "You can have size, quality, or cost: pick two." In other words, you can get a big home of outstanding quality—for a correspondingly big price tag. You can save money on your big home, but don't expect good quality workmanship. Or you can get a well-built home at a reasonable cost...but you'll sacrifice some square footage.

These are the issues that homebuyers—and homebuilders—struggle with year in and year out. We'll get into the different types of builders you can choose in a bit more depth in Chapter Two; for now, we'd just like to mention that one effect of dealing with quality, price, and square footage issues has been the proliferation of production-built homes across the nation.

Over the years, the affordability of predesigned floor plans and the flexibility of styles and colors have made production-built homes an increasingly preferred choice among new homebuyers. The sophisticated styling, modern construction techniques, and efficient scheduling of production-built homes have improved the quality and value of these homes throughout the country.

In 1975, industry experts estimated that 20% of the country's new residential homes were built by production builders. Today, advanced technology and increased awareness of the quality of production homebuilding have raised that number to an estimated 70% for production-built and semi-custom-built homes. (Naturally, estimates vary by marketplace.)

Why the demand for production-built homes? Look no further than the "price-quality-size" equation. Homeowners today are finding that production-built homes balance those three variables better than their other options. Today, new production techniques and modern technology have made it possible to give homebuyers a virtually endless array of new choices in styles, sizes, and price ranges—without their having to pay so dearly for their individual preferences. The old negative stereotypes of "cracker box" and "cookie cutter" production homes are far less common today—although the fact that poor design and shoddy workmanship still exist are more great reasons to choose your builder carefully.

Production and semi-custom builders build a lot of homes. That's why they know the many details of each stage of the construction process so well. Additionally, successful builders are continually researching and investigating new products, construction techniques, and systems that are constantly emerging from new technologies in the building industry. All of this means three things—which just happen to be the three most important things to any new homeowner:

- You can have a quality-built home at a reasonable price;
- Your home will perform well for you; and
- Your home will retain more resale value.

Professional production and semi-custom homebuilders know the typical breakdown of costs for home construction. In other words, they have a budget for everything—drywall, paint, flooring, landscaping, shingles, nails, everything—that goes into building a home, and they know what percentage of the total building cost each budget item should be.

 Our Two Cents:

How Much Home Should You Buy?

There are at least two ways to look at the money you spend on your new home. You can consider what you should spend based solely on your income...or you can take a longer-range view and consider your home an important investment.

Today, many real estate professionals and financial advisors will suggest that you should spend between two-and-a-half and four times your annual salary on your home. For example, if your income is $50,000, you should be looking at homes in the range of $125,000 to $200,000. Another formula is to consider your home as a percentage of your annual income; many advisors suggest that you should spend no more than 20 – 30% of your gross income on housing. If you make $50,000 a year, then, your mortgage payments should total between $10,000 and $15,000 annually.

These aren't bad general rules, but they have their flaws. For one, they're dependent, to some degree, upon interest rates. Obviously, when interest rates are low, you "could" afford a home near the upper end of those ranges. If you're buying when rates are extremely high, you "may" buy less home.

Here's the alternative, and it's something your mom and dad probably knew: buy as much home as you can afford.

"But won't that leave us house poor?" you ask. "Won't we be one of those sad families that has a big house and not very much furniture?"

The answer is, so what? You may start out with a big, relatively empty home. But your home is a great investment and one of the only tax deductions you have left. Investing in more home now gives you more money and more financial flexibility down the road. You'll grow into your new home—don't worry about that!

The biggest competition for housing dollars today is other consumer goods: cars, boats, computers, video game systems, and the like. We're not saying these aren't important...we're just saying they depreciate. They're not investments the way your home is.

Our advice: listen to Mom and Dad. Be a bit house poor now. You'll have more money to buy all that other cool stuff in the long run.

As an example of this budgeting process, let's say you're spending $200,000 on your new home. Production builders know that, in a $200,000 home, the budget for cabinets should be about 2% of the overall cost of the home, or $4,000.

Even the homesite you build on has a budget. In many areas of the country, your site should be approximately 20% of the total price of the home. So, using our example of the $200,000 home, the value of your homesite should be approximately $40,000.

Here's the advantage of these cost breakdowns. They create a system of balances and percentages that:

- *Allows your builder to appropriate the right materials and talent for the construction of your home.*
- *Keeps you aware of how new home construction costs are allocated.*
- *Lets you understand that there is a budget for everything that goes into building a new home.*
- *Helps ensure the quality of your home.*
- *Helps maximize the resale value of your home.*

Of course, to have budgets for everything that goes into your new home, there must be an overall budget to work from. So how do you determine the overall budget? What's the whole job going to cost?

Most builders will give you a fixed price on your new home. These builders "fit" the costs with the house before building. Other builders will give you something called a cost-plus price, which is a price figured by adding a fee onto the actual cost of a given job. While these cost-plus builders may be interested in putting the home together the way you want it, the cost in doing so is not the biggest priority. There is also no incentive for the cost-plus builder to negotiate the lowest prices and work efficiently in terms of labor and materials; in fact, just the opposite may be true. The higher the charges for labor and materials, the more money a cost-plus builder makes.

What's better? You be the judge. Just be sure you have the financial terms of your new home agreed upon before you start building it.

TYPICAL BREAKDOWN OF COSTS FOR HOUSE CONSTRUCTION

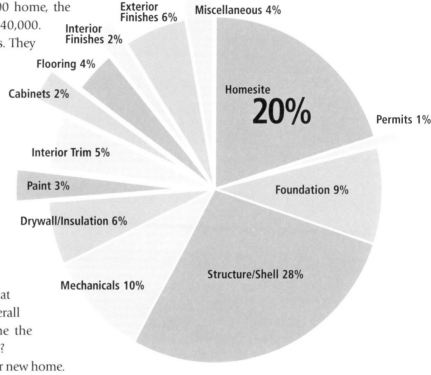

Exterior Finishes 6%
Interior Finishes 2%
Flooring 4%
Cabinets 2%
Interior Trim 5%
Paint 3%
Drywall/Insulation 6%
Mechanicals 10%
Miscellaneous 4%
Homesite 20%
Permits 1%
Foundation 9%
Structure/Shell 28%

Properly positioning the house on the homesite adds curb appeal.

The typical production or semi-custom builder has a sophisticated team of vendors, subcontractors, managers, and salespeople who are coordinated in one location. This location is usually in a master-planned development, or "community," where streets, sewers, utilities, entryways, common grounds, and amenities such as swimming pools and playgrounds are integrated and designed holistically to give residents maximum enjoyment and livability. In simpler terms, these communities are fully functional, ready-made neighborhoods.

Many production builders build homes exclusively in these predetermined locations for the sake of efficiency and quality control, whereas many custom and semi-custom builders build on individual homesites or private property commonly referred to as "scattered lots." We'll get into more specifics about the different kinds of builders and what you should expect from each in Chapter Two.

This Old House? Or That New One?

When you were deciding whether to build a new home, you probably considered buying an existing, or resale, home. At any time, there are millions of nice used homes on the market; just ask any real estate agent. So why not just buy a home that's already built?

The major reason is that there are things a new home can offer you that a used home cannot. In most cases, these things make the new home a better value. Here are a few of them:

Technology is better today.

Almost daily, the processes and materials that go into building and furnishing a new home are being improved. New and more efficient methods of construction and new products that last longer and perform more economically are being developed and discovered all the time. Reputable builders stay informed on these new materials and processes and use them in the construction of their homes. ***Better value: new home.***

Maintenance costs are lower on a new home.

Along with better materials, inspections and quality control throughout the building process help ensure that energy efficiency and durability of materials are at the highest levels possible. (See Chart 1-2.) ***Better value: new home.***

The builder helps the buyer with the finance costs.

In many cases, builders can offer financial assistance with closing costs and even mortgage rates, saving you significant money up front and throughout the life of the mortgage. _Better value: new home._

Insurance rates are lower on a new house.

Insurance companies offer "new home discounts" that have different time limits (anywhere from 2-7 years) and different rates, depending on the insurance company. _Better value: new home._

You can save tax dollars on a new home.

In many states, the property assessment tax structure has payments made in arrears; taxes aren't applied to the new homeowner until the new home is "under roof." If you're buying a new home, you might go as long as 20 months before having to pay property taxes on the completed home. This can make taxes for a new home over the first two years considerably cheaper than the taxes for a used home. (Be aware that counties within your state will vary on the definition of "under roof.") _Better value: new home._

A new home offers the latest in design and material trends.

Sure, you might be able to update an existing home with the most modern appliances, systems, and decorating ideas. Sure, you can replace old flooring and wall coverings and windows with more up-to-date options. But why bother when you can build them into the home in the first place? Besides, with a new home, all the new things are part of the mortgage, not cash out of pocket. _Better value: new home._

CHART 1-2: CRITICAL HOME COSTS

	New Home	Used Home	Monthly Savings
Taxes[1] *(first 1-2 years)*	$ 900	$ 2,400	$ 108
Financing Assistance[2]	$ 1,500	$ 0	$ 24
Utilities[3] *(2,000 sq. ft. est.)*	$ 1,300	$ 1,660	$ 30
Maintenance[4]	$ 380	$ 1,010	$ 53
Insurance[5]	$ 306	$ 360	$ 5

New Home Monthly Savings   **$ 220**

Notes: By using the amortization table rate of $6.33 for every $1,000 borrowed at 6.5% interest on a 30-year fixed rate, the monthly savings of $229 would equate to the buying power of $34,775. This means that a person could buy a new house for an additional $34,775 more than the cost of a 20-year-old used home and experience approximately the same housing costs per year. Even if the delayed tax advantages were removed from the chart above, the remaining $112 of monthly savings would still equate to buying power of almost $17,693.

This information is for illustration purposes only. The information shown here is an approximation of the savings that may be experienced when buying a new home compared with a home built approximately 20 years ago. Actual savings may be greater or smaller depending on the size, age, location, and condition of the two homes being compared. You may wish to consult your tax adviser, mortgage broker, and financial advisor for figures specific to your home purchase.

[1] FirstSource Mortgage std. tax escrow calculations for new pre-assessed homes vs. an existing assessed home
[2] The Estridge Companies financial assistance paid on 400 Series homes, assuming the assistance is used as discount points.
[3] Obtained from Cinergy/PSI® representatives comparing an older 2,000 sq. ft. home built to building code to a new The Estridge Group home.
[4] U.S. Bureau of Census, 1991 American Housing Survey
[5] Nationwide® Homeowners Policy New Home 5-year discount (20%, 18%, 16%, 15%, 14%)

A new home features newer, longer warranties.

All new homes come with warranties—and many of the appliances and systems built into new homes come with warranties of their own. You may be able to buy a warranty to protect your used home, but it simply won't match the coverage of a new home warranty. *Better value: new home.*

It's a new neighborhood for everyone.

One often-overlooked advantage of buying a new home in a new neighborhood is that everyone is new. You don't have to try to fit in with the neighbors who've lived there for 20 years or more. A new community makes it easier for you—and especially for your kids—to make new friends. *Better value: new home.*

A new home is clean and unused.

You simply don't have to worry about cleaning up someone else's messes or repairing someone else's problems when you move into a new home. Everything is clean, new, and in good working order. *Better value: new home.*

If you're keeping score, that's new home nine, used home zero.

Where Do You Go From Here?
(Or, How To Get The Most Out Of This Book)

Enough with the comparisons. It's time to get going on your new home. Which means it's time to take a closer look at what you can hope to get out of this book.

The construction of a new home is a long and detailed process. But there's no reason you can't understand it. This book has been designed to educate you on general construction practices and to help you develop a better understanding of, and comfort level with, the construction process itself. After reading this book, you should be able to talk knowledgeably about home construction, and ultimately make wise decisions about homes and homebuilders.

We'll start in Chapter Two with some basics about choosing a builder and the type of home construction that fits your needs. Chapter Three covers selecting the right location for your new home and choosing a floor plan that fits the way you live. You might think that would get us ready to build in Chapter Four, right? Wrong. We still need to discuss permits and schedules and site preparation. Chapter Five—that's where we start building the foundation for your new home. In Chapter Six, your home actually starts to look like a house, as we put up the framework, the walls, and the roof. Chapter Seven gets us through the mechanical systems: plumbing, electrical, heating and air conditioning, and more. In Chapter Eight, we'll be dressing up the interior and making everything look great. All the finishing touches are applied in Chapter Nine. Then we'll have a few more words to say about living in your new home before we close with a quiz that lets you see how much you've learned.

There's also a sample master schedule in the back of the book so you can follow the building process over time—more on the importance of this schedule a bit later. And we've created a few special signposts along the way to give you more information and help get you through trouble spots:

 On The Level gives you information about construction industry standards, building basics, and quality checkpoints.

 Hard Hat Area means "watch for falling building standards." Here we'll discuss ways some builders cut corners—and why corner-cutting is never in your best interest.

 Product Spotlight features some of the top building products on the market today—products you should definitely consider when building your new home.

 Our Two Cents features timeless wisdom about the decisions you'll have to make—particularly items that were once common knowledge that may have been lost (or at least misplaced) over the past few decades.

 Coffee Break is a place to step back from the details and consider the big picture. It's important to do this every now and again throughout the process.

Please understand that, while this book will supply you with the knowledge about what goes into building a home, it is not intended as a substitute for the expertise of an experienced builder. We meant what we said at the beginning: *your selection of a builder is the single most important decision you will make in turning your dream into a reality.*

So...let's start there.

▼ MASTER SCHEDULE NOTE: To help you gauge where you are in the construction process, we've created a timeline that runs along the bottom of the inside pages of the book, as well as the master schedule on the back flap. As you read the text, keep this schedule in mind so you can see where you are in the building process—and about how much time is left until you move into your new home.

CHAPTER TWO

Let's do even more homework so we can make good decisions.

From the bottom of your new home's foundation to the top of the roof and everywhere in between, there's one thing you must insist on: quality. Quality materials, quality products, quality workmanship: they all work together. The best carpenter in the world can't make bad lumber work as well as good lumber. The best insulation in your walls can't guarantee energy efficiency if it's installed improperly.

You get the idea. And, the fact is, the builder you choose has the ultimate responsibility for the quality of your new home. So it only makes sense to take a look at builders first.

BUILDERS

Building On The Best: Making The Right Builder Decision

Perhaps there was a time when building a home was simpler: you called the neighbors and they helped you make the log cabin. But today, everything is different. Building a modern home requires lots of specialists—and a lot more people in general. New homes today require the dynamic management of a reputable, professional homebuilder.

We can't stress this often enough. It's tough enough for a professional, conscientious builder to build a quality home; it's nearly impossible for an indiscriminate builder to do so. A successful homebuilder has strong, established relationships with many suppliers and vendors and is experienced in scheduling the multitude of workers and materials necessary

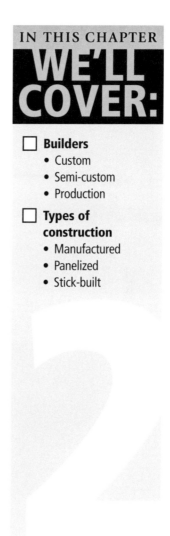

IN THIS CHAPTER

WE'LL COVER:

- ☐ **Builders**
  - Custom
  - Semi-custom
  - Production
- ☐ **Types of construction**
  - Manufactured
  - Panelized
  - Stick-built

for the construction of a home. A builder should also be experienced in the intricate and sometimes elaborate layers of specifications and regulations required throughout the construction process.

The first step in selecting a builder is to determine what kind of builder you want building your home. Today, there are three main categories of residential homebuilders:

- Custom builders
- Semi-custom builders
- Production builders

Each type of builder designs and constructs homes of varying degrees of size, complexity, and quality. It's important to know the key differences among them to determine which best meets your needs.

Custom Builders

Custom builders build one-of-a-kind homes. They typically specialize in large luxury homes that reflect the homebuyer's individual taste and lifestyle. These builders work with you extensively throughout each stage of the home design and construction process.

Contact with a custom builder begins at the design stage of the home, since each home is an original design created to the exact specifications of the homeowner. As a result of the number of one-of-a-kind features, custom homes are generally much more expensive and take longer to build than semi-custom and production homes. In addition, due to individual tastes and unique design, custom homes may not return the full cost of the personalized tastes at resale; that is, the pizza oven you had to have in your kitchen may not be the next buyer's idea of a good value.

Production Builders

In contrast to custom builders, production builders work with home styles and floor plans designed to appeal to a broad range of homeowners and lifestyles.

Production builders typically build floor plans that have been created in advance of meeting with you. These builders may have as few as four or five plans and styles to choose from, or as many as 50! By limiting your choices and working within controlled production schedules, production-built homes are typically more efficiently built and more affordable than custom or semi-custom homes. And while production builders may not be as flexible in making structural changes to a floor plan, most allow their customers to select options and the styles and colors of decorating features such as carpet, paint, cabinets, countertops, and lighting. So, just because a home is production-built doesn't mean it can't reflect your individual taste and style.

In production-built homes, the builder and construction team are intimately familiar with each floor plan and completion schedule. Changes to the floor plan will mean additional design, coordination, time, and expense. These changes can often be accommodated up front. But after you've approved your home for construction, any change will affect the materials that have been ordered, the schedules that have been put in place, the contractors who've been hired, and more. That's why a conscientious production builder will spend extra time with you before the home is started to make sure all home design decisions are final. By adhering to a set of tried-and-true designs and agreeing upon all the details up front, production builders are able to provide a home that's affordable, finished on time, and of the quality you expect.

Semi-custom Builders

Some homeowners feel that a semi-custom builder can provide a satisfactory balance between the high expense of a custom builder and the limited flexibility of a production builder. A semi-custom builder offers you a fairly wide selection of floor plans, and typically is fairly flexible in the amount and type of customization allowed. Like the production builder, the semi-custom builder works from established designs that have been perfected and can be efficiently built within established controls; however, the

▐ On The Level:

Builder Pros and Cons At A Glance

Builder Type	Pros	Cons
Custom	An original design created to your exact specifications	More expensive than semi-custom or production-built homes
	Unlimited choices in house design and construction	Takes longer than semi-custom and production-built homes
		May not recapture the full cost of the personalized elements at resale (e.g., mahogany wood ceilings, etc.)
Semi-custom	Offers you a fairly wide selection of floor plans	Difficult to keep a home affordable and in your price range when you make a large number of customizations
	Typically is flexible in the amounts and types of customization allowed	
Production	Homes are typically more efficiently built	Not as flexible in making structural changes to a floor plan
	More affordable than custom or semi-custom homes	
	Most allow you to select options and the styles and colors of decorating features such as carpet, paint, cabinets, countertops, and lighting	
	Possible to "preview" your home by visiting a model home	

Let's do even more homework so we can make good decisions.   13

Quality conscious builders usually set up a construction office at the community to provide onsite quality assurance management.

semi-custom builder offers much greater flexibility in customization (at a price, of course).

It is not uncommon for a semi-custom builder to expand a room, add a room, or change the location of a door or window to suit the needs of a particular customer. However, it should be noted that semi-custom homes present an age-old dilemma for the homeowner and builder alike: it's very difficult to keep a home affordable and in the homeowner's price range when the customer requests (and the builder agrees) to make a large number of customizations.

So how do you choose the right homebuilder for you?

You should consider a number of factors. First, prioritize your needs, desires, budget, and timeframe. (You might, for example, desire five bedrooms...but you really need only four.) You should also take the time to investigate many different builders and carefully compare the pros and cons of each. Solicit the opinions of real estate professionals, current homeowners, and other individuals who may be familiar with the reputation of the homebuilders you're considering.

Perhaps the most important thing to consider in choosing a builder is the degree of supervision the builder will have over your home construction. In other words, what is the builder's quality control system? Is there always someone supervising the site—at the site? Is the contracted and subcontracted work actually checked and inspected before the next step in the construction process? Is the home construction on a master schedule? Good, professional builders have systems in place to ensure their reputations and your satisfaction. Find out what these systems are. The more answers and information you have, the more comfortable you'll be with the builder you choose. Remember: the builder you choose has the ultimate responsibility for the quality of your new home. But it's your responsibility to choose a quality builder.

Types of Construction

Putting It All Together: How Your Home Is Built

Just as there are different types of builders who serve varying needs, there are also different types of basic construction methods. The major categories of home construction today are manufactured or modular; panelized; and stick-built construction. Let's take a quick look at all three.

Manufactured/Modular Construction

A number of years ago, some homebuilder had a bright idea: why not build homes in an indoor assembly line-type operation? It would keep all the pieces and parts out of the elements and give the builder strict quality control. The modules (or sections) of this kind of home could all be made in factories and shipped to the homesite as house sections complete with electrical, plumbing, cabinets, and even flooring.

Chances are, you've passed manufactured homes being pulled down the highway by a semi. Manufactured homes are almost 90% complete when they arrive at the homesite. Once the sections are placed on the foundation, secured, and the utilities are connected, you're ready to move in.

Modular homes are easy to identify because they arrive on wheels.

Manufactured homes are traditionally less expensive than other types of homes. They truly are mass-produced, with little or no variation from one to the next. The good news is that the quality of manufactured homes has improved quite a bit over the past several years. If affordability is the most important factor to you, manufactured housing may be the way to go.

Panelized Construction

Panelized homes are made in a factory, too...sort of. Panelized components for the frame and sheathing (usually 8' x 8') of the home are designed and factory-manufactured to meet the exact, predetermined specifications of a builder's floor plan. Then the panels are warehoused until delivery is requested on the jobsite.

When executed properly, panelization can be a fairly cost-effective method for constructing a home. But it's not without risk—the greatest of which is that, while panels are manufactured to meet exact specifications, construction itself is not an exact science. Prefabricated panel sections produced in a sterile or controlled environment to precise measurements may not fit together as perfectly as planned once they are at the construction site, primarily because foundations are not perfectly level or square. This is why a responsible builder works very closely with the foundation company and the panel manufacturer.

Let's do even more homework so we can make good decisions.   15

A panelized frame package is pre-assembled sections. These panels are cost-effectively built in a factory; however, the field measurements often require a slightly different size than the factory produced.

Stick-built Construction

The third and most preferred method of construction is stick-built construction. With stick-built construction, raw materials—in particular, the lumber for the frame—are delivered to the jobsite, where the lumber is measured, cut, and assembled board by board, according to the specifications of each individual floor plan. A section needing a board 1/4-inch shorter than the standard eight feet is not a problem with stick-built construction. The craftsmen have the opportunity to "measure twice, cut once," allowing them to make in-progress adjustments to any measurement discrepancies from foundation to framing. In short, the stick-built method allows much greater flexibility and precision at the stages of construction where accuracy is critical. This assures a sound structure and a safe, well-built home. Almost all custom homes are stick-built, as are higher-quality production homes. It's more expensive than the other types of construction. But the benefits of stick-built homes are well worth the higher price.

A stick-built frame package comes from the lumber supplier bundled in like components. The framers break down the frame pack before starting construction.

✂ Hard Hat Area:

Beware of the panelized approach to building your home. Prefabricated panels can be good for the builder, because they reduce construction time and material costs. However, if the home's foundation isn't exact—and it rarely is—the fixed panels will have to be adjusted, or the small alignment problems will become larger as the construction process continues. These adjustments are far easier to make with conventional, built-onsite lumber framing. If your builder chose prefabricated panel construction, insist on very good onsite supervision throughout the foundation and framing stages.

Whatever construction process you choose, and whichever type of builder you select to build it, the quality of the construction will ultimately determine your satisfaction with your new home. As we'll continue to remind you, the quality of the construction rests squarely on the shoulders of your builder. Don't skimp on this step. Do your homework. Ask around. Do the interviews. Remember our quality/price/size discussion? The builder you choose can be only one kind of builder; that is, you can't turn a quality/cost-conscious builder into a builder who builds big, cheap homes. This is your last chance to decide what's most important to you. There's no more critical point in the entire homebuilding process than this one.

Ready to keep going? Grab a pencil. It's time to figure out where your new home's going to be built.

CHAPTER THREE

Let's home in on the perfect site for your home.

 **LOCATION. LOCATION. LOCATION.**

The Second Most Important Decision You'll Make.

IN THIS CHAPTER

WE'LL COVER:

- ☐ **Location. Location. Location.**
- ☐ **Floor plans**
- ☐ **Site Selection**

We've already said (and said again and again) that choosing the right builder is the most important decision you'll make about your new home. Now it's time to make the next most important decision: where is your home going to be built?

Actually, a lot of people make this decision first. Perhaps you already know where you want to build, based on schools or proximity to work or simply on where you feel most comfortable. Congratulations. You're a step ahead of the game.

But, if you're still looking, how do you find just the right location for your new home? Well...you keep looking. Drive around. Think about where you might like to live and check it out. It really isn't any more complicated than that, and it's different for everyone.

What needs do you have? What amenities do you want close to home? What are the schools like? The answers to many of your questions can be found at your local builders association, with real estate professionals, at the chamber of commerce, and at the local library.

Once you've decided on an area, it's time to really get specific and start collecting information. Yep: we're talking more homework. And, because we don't want to forget what's most important, you should be making notes on builders while you're looking at neighborhoods and home styles. Find out who built the homes that interest and impress you the most.

How do you find out about builders? Here are a few tips:

- Check the real estate section in the newspaper to see where new homes are going up and who the builders are. Other sources for this information are the free new homes publications found in supermarkets and other locations.
- Don't forget to check the resale homes in the newspaper. Look at these ads to see if they list the builders' names; if builder names are showing up in resale ads, it means they probably have a reputation for building excellent homes, and the seller wants you to know.

| Start | Month 1 | Month 2 | Month 3 | Month 4 | Month 5 | Finish |

Because of the complexities involved with selecting and preparing a site on which to build a home, it has become very popular for builders to concentrate their efforts in specific housing developments or communities where the site locations are already mapped out and designed for optimal homebuilding.

- Walk through new home construction areas and developments and model homes. Look at homes at different stages of construction. Talk with anyone onsite about the homes and the builders.
- Talk with real estate professionals about builders they know and would recommend. They can also give you information about the area or site you're considering.
- Call the local builders association and get as many questions answered as you can. They're very happy to talk with any new home customer.
- Of course, you'll also want to search the Web for information about builders. Don't stop with the builders' own Web sites; look for news articles and other sources of information that may give you valuable insight into builders' reputations, as well.
- Finally, ask. Knock on doors and make phone calls to the homeowners. Don't worry too much about bugging people; most people enjoy talking about their homes and will be flattered to get your call. And you'll get no better input on a builder's quality and reputation than from the homeowners actually living in that builder's homes.

1289 CHESTNUT RIVER CROSSING

Well maintained Estridge-built two story in Oaks of Avon! 4BR, 2.5 BA. White kitchen w/laminate flooring is open to family rm w/gas frplc. Finished office/rec room w/built-ins plus lrg workshop area in lower level. Lrg master suite w/garden tub, separate shower, double sinks & walk-in closet. Extensive landscaping and mature tree line at back of property. Enjoy backyard barbecues from the screened porch, deck or spacious yard. Neighborhood pool & playground nearby. **$205,000.**

One easy way to find the quality builder in your area is to look in the newspaper's resale advertisements. A quality builder's name stays with the home even when it is resold.

Throughout your research, remember that quality and reputation are paramount. A new home under construction, or, better yet, a development under construction, is one of the best places to see homes in many stages. After reading this book, you'll know how to look for such important considerations as:

- Are the homes modular, panelized, or stick-built?
- Does there appear to be anyone onsite supervising construction?
- Is the neighborhood as clean and organized as possible while it's under construction? (They say cleanliness is next to godliness; when you're evaluating a builder, it's certainly a great indicator of quality.)
- Do the construction materials appear to have been at the site for a long time?
- Is the site under water?

The time you spend now will pay off in helping you assure the quality of the home you build. In many ways, by collecting information and investigating home construction and builders, you're laying a solid foundation for your dream.

Our Two Cents:

Do you need a real estate agent to help you find and buy a new home?

To put things in perspective, let's discuss Indianapolis, Indiana. In Indianapolis, approximately 75,000 existing homes are sold each year. Almost all of these transactions involve real estate agents for both the buyer and the seller. This would mean that there are 150,000 real estate agent "transactions" per year in Indianapolis on used/resale homes.

There are also about 15,000 new homes sold each year in the Indianapolis metro area, only about one in four of which have real estate agents involved in the transaction—and then usually only on one side of the transaction. This would equate to 3,750 real estate agent new home transactions per year. So, nearly 100 percent of used/resale homes sales are assisted by two real estate agents, while only 25 percent of new home transactions have real estate agents involved. Why the discrepancy?

There are several reasons. If you're a buyer looking for a used home, you generally need an agent to have access to all the homes that are listed. With new homes, builders have models and sales representatives onsite, which makes new homes more accessible. Secondly, in some cases, there is a tendency for real estate agents to prefer selling used homes, because the commission they earn is paid much quicker—usually in 30-45 days versus 120-150 days with new homes. Lastly, many real estate agents don't have much experience dealing with new home construction and therefore shy away from showing new homes. Some agents are afraid their buyers will ask homebuilding questions they won't be able to answer.

If you have interest in building a new home as well as looking at used homes, you certainly want to enlist the services of an agent who has experience in selling new homes. This can be done simply by asking the agents you interview how many new homes they have sold in the last one or two years.

 FLOOR PLANS

You Gotta Have A (Floor) Plan.

Assuming you didn't have a floor plan or house design before you started looking for a home and builder, the builder you choose can help determine the style, the layout, the size, and the cost of your future home. We mention floor plans now because as you look for a location and builder for your home, you'll inevitably be thinking about the type of house you want and what you want in it.

Start	Month 1	Month 2	Month 3	Month 4	Month 5	Finish

Let's home in on the perfect site for your home.

MERIDIAN COLLECTION

735

Bedroom #3
12' x 14'

Bath #2

Walk-in
Closet

Bedroom #4
14' x 10'

Walk-in
Closet

Master Bath

Down

Cathedral
Ceiling

Walk-in Closet

Elevation B & C
7' x 20'

Optional Bonus Room

Elevation A
9' x 20'

UPPER LEVEL

Open To Below

Bedroom #2
11' x 12'

Plant Ledge

Master Bedroom
14' x 17'

Garden Patio
12' x 12'

Breakfast
Nook
9' x 13'

Family Room
18' x 18'

Laundry

Kitchen
10' x 13'

Down

10' x 18'

Planning Desk

Arched Opening

Built in
Bookshelves

Arched Opening

Up   Entry
Open to Above

Living Room/Study
12' x 13'

Dining Room
11' x 14'

Optional Doors

Garage
21' x 20'

Porch

MAIN LEVEL

The actual floorplan may vary slightly due to exterior architectural selection.
© 2003 The Estridge Group

Estridge
www.estridge.com

010603

There are lots of ways to decide on a floor plan, and this aspect of choosing your new home can be as complicated or as simple as you want it to be. You might want to revisit the chart on page 13 that shows the three types of builders. Production and semi-custom builders will have a number of floor plans for you to choose from and will, in some cases, give you the option to make some changes in the plans. This makes choosing a floor plan easier and less stressful. You should note that these are not simply "generic" floor plans; the best production and semi-custom builders employ top-notch architects who design floor plans based on how people actually live in their homes.

Custom builders typically design and build homes to suit individual tastes. Sometimes you will supply the builder with the floor plan you want. If you wish to find your own floor plan, there are a number of sources, including plan books, professional architects, and designer/drafting services.

As with so many other decisions, this one is highly individual. Can you work with a floor plan that's almost exactly what you want? Or do you need to find or create one that's specifically tailored to everything you've ever wanted? Just remember: in general, the more you customize, the higher the cost.

The hardest part of building a new home is selecting from the many new designs that combine functionality with wonderful lines of sight. Now that you have picked your design, it's time to build it.

Wooded or sloped building sites have character, but the associated site conditions can add thousands of dollars to the cost of the home for tree clearing, soil compacting, retaining walls, etc.

☑ SITE SELECTION

Setting Your Sights On The Perfect Site

After you've selected your builder—and, sometimes, before you've decided on your home design—you'll need to select a homesite. While you are obviously interested in an eye-pleasing property, you also need to consider the site's technical qualities. The specific location, size, slope, accessibility, drainage, and natural environment of the site will not only determine how appropriate the site is for new home construction, but also the style and placement of your home.

Because of the peculiarities in the geography and soil composition of individual homesites, certain elements of the home's construction may be dictated by the site you choose. For example, you may favor sun streaming into your kitchen in the morning rather than in the evening. But the site you choose may force you to orient the front of your home

| Start | Month 1 | Month 2 | Month 3 | Month 4 | Month 5 | Finish |

toward the east—a problem unless you want your kitchen at the front of the home—not unheard of, but certainly a bit unusual. Other examples:

- A heavily sloped lot may require additional house reinforcement or retaining walls, or a wood deck in lieu of a concrete patio, as well as an increase in materials due to having to apply siding to parts of the home that would normally be underground.
- A high water table may prevent you from having a basement.

Your builder will have to consider a number of things when designing a home for optimum compatibility with the homesite, as well. Your builder should:

- Position the home to create the most favorable yard space.
- Position the home relative to nearby homes for privacy and "curb appeal," as well as driveway location.
- Use the natural grade of the land for aesthetics and drainage.
- Optimize views of existing features such as trees, streams, and ponds.
- Position the home for desired solar facings. (As we suggested above: do you want to have your coffee on the patio watching the sunrise, or would you rather enjoy the company of friends on your deck, watching the sunset?)
- Evaluate how the home will impact amenities shared by all homes in the community (e.g., pool, playground, picnic shelter, etc.)

Our Two Cents:

Wooded homesites are, as you might expect, quite desirable, and therefore cost more to buy. It also costs more to build on wooded sites. Your builder may also find that building around existing trees may require special access or drainage considerations. It's important to note that clearing and excavation work can cause a dramatic change in the ground drainage patterns. These changes could impact the root systems of surrounding trees and result in the death of many trees. The site preparation costs incurred by the builder could run into tens of thousands of dollars.

And, to add insult to injury, those trees that you wanted and your builder worked so hard to save just might die, anyway. We've often seen homes and even entire communities built around a big, beautiful tree that ended up dying. **Our advice:** if you're considering a wooded site, talk with your builder about the trees. Then you be sure to take good care of them after you move in.

What is the difference between a developer and a builder? The developer buys and zones the land, installs the utilities, and sells homesites. Builders secure the building permit and build the home.

Obviously, all of these technical and aesthetic homesite considerations help determine the position and style of the home to be constructed; in other words, your site may dictate whether you build a ranch-style home, two-story home, or a home with a walkout basement. So, while some people choose their floor plan first, it's easy to understand why site selection may precede the selection of your floor plan.

Master-planned communities

You're probably familiar with new home communities where all the homes are of a uniform style and all in a similar price range; they've been around for decades. But today, some builders are involved in the design and development of master-planned communities. A master-planned community

Often, developers buy large pieces of land and zone them for multiple house types. They do this to lower homeowner costs by spreading the cost of engineering, construction, and amenities across more homes.

A community is more than houses. A community is a way of life. Some developers may cut costs by skimping on the community amenities.

is a location where homes of multiple styles, each designed for a different demographic group, are integrated into one cohesive community. These communities generally share some theme and often share common amenities or recreational areas. It's almost as if, instead of creating a new neighborhood or subdivision, the builder is creating a new town, with homes ideal for young families, singles, couples, empty nesters, large families, and others.

A wonderful advantage of building in a master-planned community is that you know the lifestyle you and your family will enjoy even before you start building your new home. You can get a great feel for this kind of community by driving around and asking the people who live there what they like about it.

Most important, master-planned communities are fully engineered; that is to say, all utilities (sewer, water, electric) are in place. Roads, sidewalks, street signs, and even amenities such as parks, pools, and recreational areas are included. Homesites have already been laid out and assigned for homebuilding. Even the community entryways are created with a style and quality that is consistent with the rest of the development, making you feel like you've arrived home when you pull into the neighborhood—not just when you pull into your driveway.

Where are you going to build your home and who is going to build it for you? These are the two questions only you can answer. The more knowledge and information you have, the more you're assured of having the answers that will give you the home you want. And once you make these decisions, it's time to put the building process in motion. That's what we're going to do in Chapter Four.

⚒ Hard Hat Area: Watch for falling building standards.

Are all builders created equal? Of course not; yet, when comparing new homes, buyers often look at square footage and little else.

There are many ways to build a new home—remember our quality/price/size discussion—but really only two philosophies about what's included with that home. Some production builders prefer to build "stripped down" homes, then charge buyers to add in the things they really want—fireplace, a better grade of carpet, garden tub, etc. There's nothing wrong with this philosophy, if you know it going into the decision-making process. But be advised that for some "homes starting in the $120s," you may have to add $20 or $30 thousand worth of extras to create the home you really want. In addition, builders who work this way will use often their upgrades as a profit center. If it's not included in the base price of the home, it's often going to be marked up significantly.

Other production builders have the philosophy that they would rather create homes with more features included, since they understand these are things that the vast majority of their buyers are going to want, anyway. These features—fireplaces, interior trim, wood windows, and many others— may seem to make the home more expensive. But these features are normally included at a lower cost. In other words, by the time you add these features to the stripped-down builder's home, the "less expensive" home may actually end up costing a lot more.

Finally, beware of empty square footage. Some production builders lure unwary buyers by promising "more home" for less money. But you don't get anything for nothing. More home can mean less in many other important features. These homes are often quite large but they're just as often devoid of character and, more important, devoid of quality. To get more square footage, builders have to cut corners—often quite literally. How do they do it? Read on.

Let's home in on the perfect site for your home.

As you've seen, many of the first steps in building a new home don't require a hammer or saw—just a discerning eye, a fair amount of good judgment, and a willingness to dig for information. So now that you've selected a reputable builder, a homesite, and a floor plan, you're ready to start the real digging, right?

Not quite. There are still several steps to take before you break ground on your new home. We promise: we're almost there...

☑ PLOT PLANS AND BUILDING PERMITS

The Plot Thickens

Once you and your builder have decided on the exact location for your home and the exact floor plan to be built, your builder must come up with a plot plan. The plot plan is a technical diagram created by an engineer that details the precise measurements and layout of the house in relation to property boundaries, public easements, water and sewer lines, electrical transformer boxes, etc. Of course, there are those aesthetic considerations we considered in Chapter Two, too. Thoughtful placement of the home can dramatically improve the quality and usability of the yard, the way the sunlight enters your home, and other important factors.

After the plot plan has been prepared, the builder submits the plan package (plot plan, blueprints, permit request forms, etc.) to the appropriate municipality to obtain the actual building permit. As part of the permitting process, a zoning or planning board must

IN THIS CHAPTER

WE'LL COVER:

- ☐ **Plot plans and building permits**
- ☐ **Scheduling**
- ☐ **Homesite preparation**
- ☐ **Clearing the site**
- ☐ **Stake-out**
- ☐ **Temporary electrical power**

Start	Month 1	Month 2	Month 3	Month 4	Month 5	Finish

Delays in the home-building process can be frustrating for you—and costly for your builder. Due to certain fixed costs, personnel costs, and the cost of financing, every day your home construction is delayed costs your builder $150 to $500 or more. So it's in everyone's best interest to keep the job on schedule. (Of course, if you selected that cost-plus builder, you are the one paying for the delay...and your builder may actually profit!)

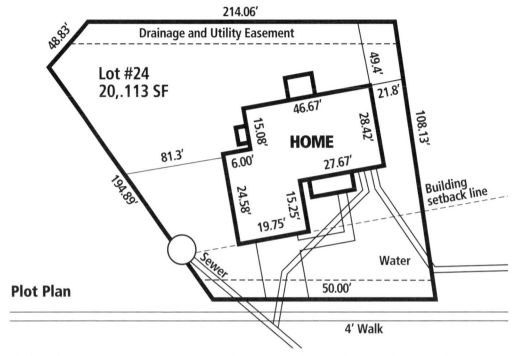

Plot Plan

The floor plan outline is electronically placed on the homesite to make sure it does not conflict with the easements or setback lines. Once fit is verified, a paper copy called a Plot Plan is produced.

certify that a proposed home is within the bounds of local zoning ordinances. Additionally:

- A building official will have to certify that the house plans meet all local building requirements.
- An architectural review board in a subdivision may have to approve the aesthetic quality of the design of the home, considering such factors as permit applications, construction plans, plot plans, elevations, paint colors, landscaping designs, and samples of siding or roof materials.
- If the builder or homeowner needs to drill a well or install a septic tank on the site, advance permits must be secured from the local health department.

Yes, there is some red tape to go through in building a new home. The approval process and issuance of the building permit and other permits take from one day to one month and can cost anywhere from a few hundred dollars up to several thousand dollars, depending on the municipality. But this is another reason you've chosen a professional, reputable homebuilder who knows all about the permitting processes and can take you through them easily and painlessly. Most production builders actually do all the permit work, so you don't have to do anything yourself in this area.

☑ SCHEDULING

Putting The Plan On Paper

When all the necessary permits have been received, the entire construction information package is ready to be delivered to the construction supervisor. Now it's time to schedule the construction of your new home. A builder's efficiency and success in building a quality home hinge on the ability to coordinate and orchestrate all the activities taking place during construction. This ability to orchestrate is a leading indicator of whether the builder you've selected is really equipped to do the job.

Scheduling of the many different vendors, subcontractors, and specialists can be a complex and dynamic process. That's why the experienced professional builder of today has developed a *master schedule*. A master schedule divides the processes of construction into efficient and manageable blocks, setting the times for the purchase and delivery of materials, the work orders for the different subcontractors and craftsmen, and the inspections associated with each stage of the home's construction. Everything's included in the master schedule, from the signing of the initial purchase agreement to your final closing. Time, after all, is money—and the master schedule puts everything out there in black and white.

The master schedule gives your builder a number of other advantages, too:
*   By dividing activities into manageable pieces your builder can systematically review the quality and efficiency at *each step of construction.*
*   Scheduling the most efficient numbers of crews in the home at the same time allows your builder to make subcontractors more accountable for their responsibilities, helping set high standards of workmanship and integrity. Subcontractors also appreciate the convenience of not being crowded by the presence of too many workers. The master schedule makes it easier for them to do their jobs efficiently and expertly.

The building permit is required for residential construction. The permit is generally displayed in a visible, accessible place. The city inspector uses the permit to note his approval or needed changes.

⌊ On The Level:

Many builders stake out a home the day before the footers are dug—or sometimes even earlier the same day. Why? Because any stake being moved by playful kids or extreme weather conditions would mean the homesite would have to be re-surveyed, costing hundreds of dollars. Or, even worse, the home construction could start with incorrect measurements.

And these measurements are more than a little exact. Measurements are made to the 1/100th of a foot; in fact, so precise are the measurements that you will find a nail driven into a spot on the top of the stake marking the precise spot from which the measurements should be taken!

Let's do the final groundwork before breaking ground.

- A master schedule keeps delays to a minimum and gives your builder the ability to most efficiently adjust the elements of the schedule when delays are unavoidable.
- With a master schedule, your builder can schedule materials for "just-in-time" delivery. Because many components of the home are engineered and manufactured offsite, where conditions are ideal and more conducive to precision, the deliveries of these components must be carefully planned to coincide with the construction activity. The object of a just-in-time construction schedule is for the materials and components to arrive on the jobsite immediately before their installation. This allows your builder to minimize losses due to weather damage, theft, or confusion caused by an overly crowed jobsite.

An example of a master schedule is enclosed on the back flap of this book. It's been designed so you can easily follow the construction process as we detail it here for you. To follow the schedule as you read, simply fold open the back flap.

Once all the preliminary administrative and legal issues have been addressed and the master schedule has been set up, you can begin the actual process of preparing the homesite for construction. Ready? Let's move some dirt!

✅ HOMESITE PREPARATION

The Artist Prepares His Canvas

Just as you wouldn't start painting a masterpiece on a dirty canvas, a builder can't start working on your new house until the homesite is properly prepared for the construction process. Preparation involves clearing the site, staking the site to identify the exact placement of your new home, and bringing electrical power to the site. Let's examine these steps now.

Clearing the site

When you cut the grass, you know you're supposed to first walk the yard and pick up all the rocks and sticks so the yard is cut properly and you don't harm your mower. Well, it's the same with preparing your homesite. Only more so. All obstacles that would impair building your new home need to be removed. This is simply called *clearing the site,* and involves the removal of any trees, large rocks, and debris that hinder the construction of your new home or present safety concerns.

The homesite is cleared conscienciously in preparation of home construction.

In addition, your homesite is leveled in preparation for the next step in the construction process at this time. No, this doesn't mean that a bulldozer makes your homesite look like a parking lot, taking out everything in its path; after all, you've selected a builder who understands that the aesthetic qualities of your home include the site it's built on. (You have selected this kind of builder, haven't you?) Any trees, large rocks, or other natural elements that can be left alone will be. However, understand that the builder will need at least a 10-foot work area around the house perimeter—from the footings out—to build your home. Anything inside this work area has got to go.

Stake-out

Once the site is cleared and leveled, your builder is ready to stake out your home. The stake-out is the process by which a surveyor engineer,

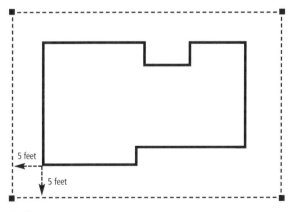

Stake-out
Laying out the big-box with only four stakes located 5' out and 5' over from the actual corner. This keeps the stakes a safe distance from the construction activities.

Let's do the final groundwork before breaking ground.

The onsite builder checks the big box stakes against the engineer's lot plan to verify the house's proper location

usually the same person who produced the plot plan, marks the corners of the home, usually with wooden stakes, identifying the exact placement of the home on the lot.

It's common for the surveyors to stake out the home using the "big box" technique, at which only the outermost corners of the home are staked, rather than staking every turn in the perimeter of the foundation. The stakes marking the four corners of the house are set back a predetermined distance, usually five to ten feet from the true corner positions. (This sometimes creates confusion among homeowners when they see their home being staked out and it appears that the house will be sitting partially on the neighbor's yard!) The reason for staking five or ten feet back from the actual position of the foundation is to provide room for the excavating equipment to maneuver and perform the trenching work without disturbing the true positions of the stakes. Also, by using the big box technique, your builder minimizes the number of measurements that the surveyor has to make, thus improving efficiency and saving money.

So isn't there a chance this will cause a mistake in measurements later? Not really. When the subcontractor comes to dig the footings, the blueprints are referred to before measuring in from the big box line to establish the exact configuration of the foundation. These blueprints show the exact location of the home on the site. So as long as you've hired a conscientious builder, there's no need for worry.

Temporary electrical power

Have you noticed that temporary pole fitted with an electrical meter and connected to the nearest electrical transformer box? Don't worry. That's not how the electricity will come into your new home. This temporary electric pole provides power to the home until the permanent electrical service is connected.

Up to this point in the construction process, there hasn't been much need for electrical power. But after the stake-out has been completed, the heavy construction activities begin to occur at a whirlwind pace. Now it becomes necessary for your builder to arrange for a source of power so all those people with saws and drills and other power tools can get to work.

Now that the homesite is cleared and leveled, the home is staked out, and the temporary source of electricity is set up, your builder is ready to begin work on the foundation. It's the moment you've been waiting for. Grab your camera and shovel: it's time to break ground on your dream.

A temporary power pole and meter are placed for the construction of the home.

Let's do the final groundwork before breaking ground.   35

CHAPTER FIVE

(At long last) we actually start building your home.

Feeling pretty good about yourself now, aren't you? You've made it through all the homework, the initial paperwork, and the site preparation. At last, the actual construction of your new home is ready to begin. If you think it's been an exciting process up to this point, you ain't seen nothin' yet.

Open the back flap of this book and take note of where we are on the master schedule. As you can see, we're still in the first month of a four- to five-month process. So while construction is progressing on schedule, and you have reason to get excited, let's pace ourselves. We still have a long way to go, and you're going to need your strength.

IN THIS CHAPTER

WE'LL COVER:

☐ **Footings**

☐ **Types of foundations**
- Slab
- Crawlspace
- Basement

☐ **Final foundation details:**
- Backfill
- Sewer
- Waterlines

The very first physical element required in the construction of your home is the foundation structure. Remember how we've been saying that choosing the right builder is the single most important consideration in building your new home? Well...the foundation is the single most critical element in your home. The foundation provides the base on which the home will rest and is subject to extreme amounts of stress from compression and weathering. It has to be right; if the foundation is out of square, problems will be compounded as the contractors who build on it have to make adjustments to compensate for the initial inaccuracies. When the foundation of the home is faulty, the integrity of the entire structure is placed in jeopardy. A faulty foundation can be repaired and made as good as new, but usually only at great cost.

Start	Month 1	Month 2	Month 3	Month 4	Month 5	Finish

L | On The Level:

How deep do you dig footings? Depth is primarily determined by the frost line, and so it varies dramatically by region. It's critically important to set the base of your home below the frost line so the freeze/thaw cycle doesn't affect the home's structure.

The footing contractor uses electronic equipment, the blueprints, and the big-box stakes to locate where the footings are to be placed.

☑ FOOTINGS

Giving Your Home a Firm Footing

Repeat with us, one more time: *the foundation is the single most critical element in your home.* And the first step in creating your foundation is trenching the footings. Footings are the trenched areas filled with concrete that serve as the base or sub-foundation on which the foundation will rest. Positioned around the perimeter of the house, the footings are usually several inches wider than the foundation wall to provide additional stability.

Creating the footings is a five-step process that consists of:

- Mapping the footing trenches
- Digging
- Notifying the local building inspector and getting approval
- Pouring the concrete
- Allowing the concrete time to harden

Let's look at each step in a bit more detail. (Hey—it's really important. Remember?)

Mapping

The first step in creating the foundation is to transfer the blueprint onto the ground with great precision. This task is performed by experienced footing specialists who use the blueprints, survey stakes, and good old-fashioned geometry to trace—usually with string or chalk—the footing lines onto the ground to show where the digging should occur.

Digging the trenches

Once the footing lines have been marked, workers dig or trench an area that's usually 16 inches wide for a two-story home and 12 inches wide for a ranch home, and about two feet deep. "Dug" usually means the work was done with a narrow backhoe shovel; "trenched" means it was performed with a machine specially designed to dig this size trench. The depth and size of the trench can vary, depending on slope, frost line, soil, or other construction reasons.

Getting approval

Once the footings are trenched or dug, your builder will notify the local building inspector. The footing trenches should be inspected prior to pouring the concrete to ensure proper depth, width, and soil stability.

Pouring the concrete

Upon inspection and approval, your builder can begin pouring the actual concrete into the trenches. Most builders use a high-compression concrete that can withstand the tremendous weight of the home and its contents; this concrete is free flowing and pours nearly level, then is hand finished, if necessary. In some cases, your builder will use lumber forms to contain the concrete while it sets. These forms are removed once the concrete sets.

The footing contractor then traces out the footing outline and begins the trenching or digging process. The footings are placed below the frost line.

Some builders believe that all living space should have footings under the space for structural stability and to reduce air infiltration. While some builders...

...prefer to save money by 'hanging' the living space from the exterior walls without a costly foundation supporting the structure.

(At long last) we actually start building your home.

Allowing the concrete to harden

After the concrete has been poured into the footing trenches, it needs to cure, or harden, for a short period of time. The length of the curing process is determined by climate and weather. As a rule, the lower the temperature, the longer curing time required. Once the concrete has cured, your builder can build the foundation wall.

TYPES OF FOUNDATIONS

Your Most Important Element—In Three Popular Styles

There are three basic types of foundations commonly used in new home construction: slab, crawlspace, and basement foundations. The type of foundation you choose has a lot to do with the design of your new home and your own preference, but other considerations—the slope of the lot, the water table, and the condition of the soil—can be factors, as well. Here's a quick look at each type of foundation.

Slab foundation

A *slab foundation* is a flat layer of concrete positioned on two courses of blocks set directly over the footings and the underlying ground. Many builders choose to use a slab foundation because of its efficiency; the slab is the floor of the home. Slabs are comparatively less difficult to construct than basement and crawl space foundations, and consequently, are less expensive. Typically, a slab foundation requires a flat lot.

The first step in constructing a slab foundation is to have the block masons transfer the blueprint information to the footings by stretching a chalk line taut and marking straight lines on the footings to serve as guides while laying two or more courses (or layers) of blocks. This process is known as "stringing" or "chalking" the job.

On the top row of foundation blocks, the mason will insert anchor bolts into the mortar between two blocks. The anchor bolts are spaced no more than every six feet (one foot from corners) and protruding vertically from the foundation. Anchor bolts are considered the preferred method for securing the frame of the house to the actual foundation because of their strength and effectiveness at restricting any movement. For most homes, a crew can lay the foundation block in about a day.

After the trench has been inspected, the concrete is poured with high compression concrete and hand troweled. These footings serve as the base or the foundation of the home.

At this point, most builders will check carefully to see that the foundation block has been properly constructed. They will check for:

- Square corners
- A level surface
- The correct number of anchor bolts
- General quality of workmanship
- Accurate diagonal dimensions using geometric formulas

This foundation block will also serve as a form for the slab, containing the poured concrete as it hardens. Assuming the foundation block is up to standards, your builder must now take care of some other preliminary activities before the actual slab layer can be poured.

Before the slab: plumbing and electrical

Since a slab foundation doesn't provide for any access underneath the concrete, your builder must now install any preliminary mechanical systems, such as plumbing and electrical systems, that run through the slab area. On homes with crawlspaces and basements, these systems don't have to be installed until later...although, on basement homes, the sump pump pit needs to be installed before the slab floor is poured.

But let's stick with the slab for now and start with the plumbing. First, the plumbers start by installing PVC drain lines for sinks, tubs, toilets, the washing machine, and the water heater overflow. The drain lines are placed directly on the ground where the slab will be poured and are run to their appropriate positions in the slab, then fitted with a plastic cover. The cover serves to keep the lines free of concrete when the slab is being poured.

Why do you install drain lines first? So that they don't rise over other lines, which would give you improper drainage flow. The precise slope of each line is critical to proper gravity

Foundations must be placed below the frost line for the region in which the home is built. This is one reason why basements are built in the north while slab foundations are common in the south.

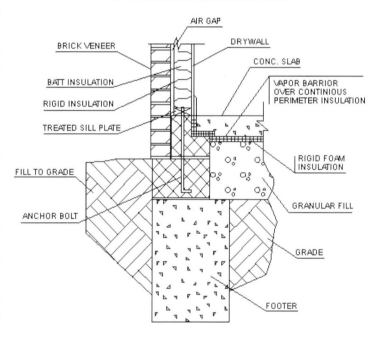

Slab Foundation Cross Section

The block is delivered just in time for the block mason to build the foundation walls.

The block mason uses the blueprints to transfer the block layout to the poured footers via chalk outlines.

The block is then placed along the chalk lines.

The mason sets the anchor bolts into the block and mortars them into place.

drainage. The drainage line will eventually be hooked up to the sanitary sewer lines buried near the street. More on this later.

Next, the plumbers will run a 3/4-inch water supply line, commonly referred to as the water service line, from the front yard water meter outside the home to the location of the water heater inside the home. Then, from the water heater, 1/2-inch copper supply lines are run to predetermined points in the slab under the locations of sinks, tubs, showers, and other appliances and fixtures requiring hot water.

Supply lines that carry water to each water fixture in your home are usually protected with a foam jacket at the point at which they stick out of the slab. Each line is then fitted with a plastic sleeve—blue for cold water, red for hot—that helps tradespeople better identify individual water lines later on in the process.

After the initial plumbing systems have been put into place, it's time for the electricians to do their thing. They install any electrical lines that are required to run through the slab before it is poured. This usually occurs only in the case of a kitchen island or other floor-mounted receptacles. Wiring in the slab is usually encased in flexible protective metal tubing

The drain lines (white) are installed first to achieve proper downward slope.

called conduit. The conduit is set in the slab area above the water and sewer lines.

Pouring the slab

Now that all the foundation blocks are in place and all the necessary plumbing and electrical rough-ins are complete, your builder can prepare the foundation for the slab. To prepare the foundation area, a small earthmover or bobcat fills the area with fill sand or gravel to a point four inches below the rim of the block foundation. Then the foundation wall area is insulated both horizontally and vertically. Once all the pieces are in place, a vapor barrier is installed over the fill and insulation.

Finally, the concrete is poured carefully over the fill sand or gravel, insulation board, and a plastic film vapor barrier. The actual slab surface is poured flush with the top of the

Installer performs quality assurance on crew's work by using a level to check for proper slope in drain line.

foundation block. As the concrete begins to harden, workers will machine and/or hand trowel the surface to close the pores in the concrete and form a smooth, hard surface. Smoothing the surface seals in the moisture that cures the concrete and minimizes cracking and scaling.

When the plumbing is completed, perimeter insulation is installed. Then sand or gravel is used to fill the blocked area. A vapor barrier will cover the fill before the concrete is poured.

The plumbing lines are precisely located to protrude through the slab at the sinks, tubs, shower, and water heater.

The three certain things in life; death, taxes and concrete cracks.

If you're out at the homesite, you may notice some hairline cracks in the concrete. Don't worry about these; they're rarely severe enough to warrant concern. It's very common for concrete to form these hairline cracks when it cures. As the moisture in the concrete evaporates, the volume of the slab will contract slightly, causing cracks to form. All concrete goes through this natural curing process and there is nothing even the world's best, most conscientious builder can do to prevent cracks. Although the cracks may look like flaws, they do absolutely nothing to compromise the integrity or strength of the structure. However, if the crack is larger than 1/4-inch in width, your builder may want to use a silicone caulk to fill it.

Crawlspace foundations

A crawlspace foundation is very much like a slab foundation, except that two additional courses of block are used to build up the side-walls. Then instead of pouring concrete, a wood floor system is built on top of the block. The raised block walls and wood floor create a space you can crawl through to get access to the underside of the home—thus, the name "crawlspace." Let's look at the process in a bit more detail.

With a crawlspace foundation, blocks for the walls are stacked higher—usually four rows instead of two. (Some builders today are pouring "short walls" instead of using blocks. You'll learn more about this technique later in this chapter.) Your builder will usually cover the soil in a crawlspace with a layer of pea gravel or other fill material, then apply a layer of plastic vapor barrier over the gravel to reduce moisture and the possibility of wood damage. Then the wood floor is built on the blocks or walls, at least 18 inches above the ground, by building code. (We'll talk more about constructing the floor in Chapter Five.)

In a crawl space, the wood floor structure is held up by either courses of block or poured short walls.

On The Level:

Before pouring the slab foundation concrete, a conscientious builder will insulate a slab in three ways: first, by placing Owens Corning FOAMULAR® rigid foam insulation board vertically around the inside perimeter of the block; second, by placing the insulation board flat over the fill in a one-foot wide strip around the inside perimeter of the block; and third, by covering the entire area with a heavy plastic vapor barrier. The first two steps prevent the frost line from invading the area below the concrete slab floor. The third inhibits ground moisture from rising up through the floor.

When pouring the garage floor, it's a good idea for your builder to form a slight slope (two inches, back to front) to allow rain and snow that melts from parked cars to drain outside the garage.

Why would you want your home on a crawlspace foundation instead of a slab? Some reasons include:

- It's easier to install and service your mechanical systems.
- Crawlspaces are more compatible with basements than slabs; some homes have partial basement foundations and partial crawlspace foundations.
- If your homesite has a slight grade and one side must be built up higher than the other, a crawlspace is a natural solution.

What's the downside? Well, crawlspaces are generally more costly than slabs. Based on a home size of 1,600 square feet, a crawlspace will cost $4,000-$6,000 more than a slab foundation.

(At long last) we actually start building your home.

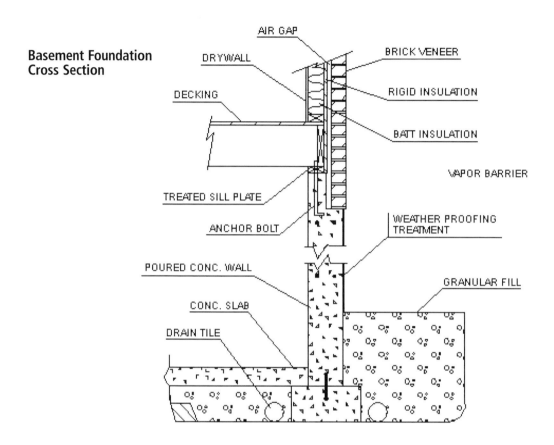

Basement Foundation Cross Section

AIR GAP

DRYWALL

BRICK VENEER

RIGID INSULATION

DECKING

BATT INSULATION

VAPOR BARRIER

TREATED SILL PLATE

ANCHOR BOLT

WEATHER PROOFING TREATMENT

POURED CONC. WALL

GRANULAR FILL

CONC. SLAB

DRAIN TILE

Basements

Basement foundations are very popular with homeowners because of the large amount of space they add to a home. With a basement foundation, the basement floor is typically a concrete slab. Masonry or poured concrete walls, usually eight or more feet high, support the main level of the house, allowing the basement area to be used for storage or additional living area.

And added room isn't the only reason to build a home on a basement foundation. On a homesite with a severe slope, a basement foundation may be the only way for a builder to accommodate the differences in ground elevation. It is also possible that your builder may be required to place the footings of the foundation much deeper than normal because of particular soil conditions or composition, thus making a basement foundation mandatory. Furthermore, in some parts of the country, the frost line is so deep that once the footings are dug, a basement is the only foundation that makes sense.

It's wise for your builder to use flexible copper tubing as supply lines to achieve a continuous connection, without seams or joints, directly to each destination. Minimizing the number of seams and joints helps minimize the risk of ruptured lines and leaky joints within the slab.

Due to basement footings being placed deeper into the ground, builders should place drain tiles on the interior and the exterior of the footings to drain foundation water to the sump pump pit. Also in this picture, the concrete by the shovel is a "thicken slab" footing which will align with the basement support post.

Basements are dug larger than the actual basement size. The contractor must dig the basement hole at least two feet wider all the way around to provide room to work and place the wall forms. Some codes require an even larger overdig for worker safety.

Before forming the basement walls, your builder should place perforated drainage pipes along the perimeter of the footing, both inside and outside. This drainage pipe system directs water away from the foundation to a sump pump located below the basement floor.

When designing the basement foundation, your builder should pay special attention to its particular configuration, including the future layout of the heating, ventilation, and cooling system; electrical system; and water and waste lines. Do you plan to use your basement as additional finished living space? If so, make sure your builder knows. The very most economical place to locate all these systems is the center of the basement—which can effectively turn your large living area into four little ones. If you do want to use the basement as a finished living space, it would be best to have all these systems located to one side so they

Once the walls have adequately hardened, the wall forms are removed.

Basement wall forms are set on top of the footings and filled with concrete. The anchor bolts are then set into the freshly poured walls.

can be walled off from the finished area.

It's also critical to properly engineer and reinforce the basement walls to meet internal and external structural challenges. Your basement walls must be able to support the weight of the entire house and its contents. External pressure also exists, due to a difference in the pressure between the outside soil and the inside living area. For all these reasons, it's essential to reference your local building codes for the required thickness of basement walls in your area.

Block is sometimes used for basement walls, but the preferred method of wall construction involves pouring concrete into temporary forms, which will be removed later, after the concrete has adequately hardened. In fact, pouring walls is becoming such a routine and successful practice that some builders are even pouring the crawlspace "short walls," and slab foundation walls, too. Pouring the walls saves the builder time and makes it unnecessary to bring another tradesperson—the block mason—to the jobsite just to do the crawlspace walls.

Before the basement wall concrete hardens, the system for fastening the frame to the

The concrete floor is poured about one week after the wall forms are removed. Placing the sump pump pit in a corner may increase the cost of the HVAC system; however, it maximizes continuous floor space in the basement.

After a protective rubberized water barrier is applied to the basement walls, a fibrous board is installed to protect the barrier during the backfill process.

foundation, preferably anchor bolts, is positioned vertically on top of the wall. Be patient here; it takes approximately five to 20 days for the concrete in the basement walls to adequately cure.

Since the basement walls are built well below ground level, the builder must also take extra precautions to thoroughly waterproof them. One very effective basement waterproofing method consists of a rubberized membrane that is heated and then applied directly to the concrete wall in a spray form. This rubberized material cools and essentially forms a shrink-wrapped coating around the basement's exterior. After this membrane has cooled, a protective insulation board is attached to the exterior of the walls. This board is a semi-rigid, thermal insulation board usually made from glass fibers. Its principal purpose is to protect the waterproof membrane from puncture and damage during backfill. The board also allows water to drain more freely down the side of the wall to the footing drain.

Next, the support system for the main floor is put into place. The type of flooring system will depend on your builder and the distance the floor has to span. We'll talk more about this in Chapter Six.

Anchor bolts are the means by which the wood structure is attached to the concrete foundation.

Obviously, there are many advantages of having a basement. But you should know that building a basement is far more involved than building another type of foundation; the excavation, poured concrete walls, and curing time are all costly additions to the process. You should expect to pay an additional $20,000 or more to add a basement to your new home.

✔ FINAL FOUNDATION DETAILS: BACKFILL, SEWER, AND WATER LINES

Finishing Off The Foundation

We're just about ready to start framing your home. But before your builder proceeds to the framing stage, a few miscellaneous items related to the foundation and excavation need to be addressed.

First, the builder will perform the backfill. The backfill is the process by which approximately two feet of stone is put into the hole around the foundation walls; then, a

The water pit is usually located in the front yard. This is where the water meter unites the water main and home service line. The home's water service can be turned on or off from this location.

Gravel then dirt are backfilled into the basement overdig. The overdig is necessary to give the wall contractors room to work. The backfilled area may settle during the first year of home ownership, requiring refilling.

bulldozer pushes the previously excavated dirt back into the hole around the foundation wall. Your builder should backfill up to the top of the foundation wall, leaving a slight grade away from the home, which will allow water to run off and away from the house. (You should keep in mind that there's a lot of air in this dirt, which will cause it to settle eventually. You'll likely need to reestablish the proper grade during the first few years.) By leaving a few inches of foundation wall block exposed, the wood elements of the home are above the ground and away from moisture.

Next, your builder will connect the water service line that transports water from the water main located near the street curb to the water meter, and then into your home. The water service line is made of 3/4-inch copper pipe. Builders typically refer to the location where the water meter connects to the service line as the water pit. The actual water meter is installed by your local water company at the time of service connection.

Finally, your builder will make arrangements for the sewer lateral and water service line to be located. The sewer lateral is the primary pipe that transports the sewage from your house

The sewer clean out access point is usually located next to the home's foundation at the point that the sewer line exits the home.

to the sewer main located along the street. The sewer main is the final line that transports the waste out of the community. The sewer lines inside the home typically consist of four-inch diameter PVC pipe that exit at an inconspicuous point below ground on the side of the home.

At this time, your builder may also install an exterior sewer cleanout at the point where the sewer lateral exits the home. The sewer cleanout is a convenience that enables plumbers to service the line from outside the home should the internal drain lines become obstructed.

With the final foundation details complete, the most crucial element in your new home construction is in place and ready to support your dream. While your new home might not look like more than a concrete stage or box at this point, the critical importance of a professionally built, high-quality foundation can't be over-emphasized. Now we're ready for the real fun—watching your home take shape—to begin.

⚒ Hard Hat Area: Watch for falling building standards.

Maybe you've heard horror stories about homeowners who have built their dream homes only to find that, a couple of years down the road, they've been invaded by mold. This situation is not as uncommon as you might expect—and it can cost tens of thousands of dollars and months of frustration and heartache to fix.

Your builder is supposed to pour basement walls thick enough (at least eight inches) to allow for the width of the brick, wall-framing 2x4s, and sheathing that sits atop them—plus approximately a one-inch airspace to keep moisture off the wall sheathing and allow it to drain in the airspace between the brick and the sheathing. How does water get in there? Brick and mortar are naturally porous materials, so some moisture will get behind them. (Think about it: have you ever seen a dam made of brick? We didn't think so.)

Some builders may try to cut corners by pouring their concrete walls thinner. This means the brick has to sit directly against the sheathing, allowing moisture that wicks through the brick direct access to the sheathing and creating an environment more conducive to mold growth. When moisture and warm temperature combine with a source of food—that could be the sheathing—mold may grow.

One way builders will try to address this potential problem is by using a vapor barrier over the sheathing. This is a great idea—but, by itself, is not the best protection against mold. The best answer is to make sure your home has an airspace between the brick and the sheathing. It will cost a little more now in terms of concrete...but it can save you plenty down the road.

Our Two Cents:

Before we get too far along in the building process, we ought to talk for just a minute about...damage.

Damage to your home during construction is inevitable. Windows are going to get broken. Countertops are going to need fixing. Someone's going to swing a 2x4 and scratch up a freshly painted wall.

The good news is, your builder knows about these things. And things take time to fix. Remember, your builder is working on a master schedule. It might take a couple of weeks to get a new window ordered and delivered. So if you see a broken window and tell your builder about it, be patient. The damage will be corrected.

The better news is, you have many inspection points before you close on your home...and warranties to help ensure the quality of materials and workmanship after you've moved in. Don't let construction damage worry you. It happens, and will be made right. And it's another good argument against hiring a cost-plus builder.

CHAPTER SIX

Your Home Begins To Look Like A House

To this point, your new home hasn't looked much like a house. But that's about to change. It's time to start building your home's structural framework: its skeleton, if you will. And now it's beginning to look like the house you imagined. Soon you'll be walking through the place, trying to make decisions about where you'll put the television and how much new furniture you need for the living room.

Three systems—the floor, the framing, and the roofing—collectively serve as the basic skeletal structure of the home. Typically referred to as the "rough carpentry" phase of construction, these systems have a tremendous impact on the integrity of the structure and the success of procedures following their installation. That's why it's so important to employ experienced, knowledgeable craftsmen who understand not only the principles and practices of their trades, but also the roles these systems play in the entire construction process.

✔️ FRAMING

Skeleton Keys: The Fine Points Of Framing

Your house's frame is its basic structure—the underlying bones of your home. This framework provides a surface on which the roof can be placed and the walls can be set. It's

IN THIS CHAPTER

WE'LL COVER:

- ☐ **Framing**
  - Floor systems
  - Wall framing
  - Sheathing
  - Roof systems
- ☐ **Exterior doors and windows**
- ☐ **Exterior trim**
- ☐ **Roofing**
  - Attic vents
- ☐ **Outside appearance**
  - Siding
  - Painting and caulking
  - Gutters and down spouts
  - Exterior concrete

Start		Month 2	Month 3	Month 4	Month 5	Finish

The lumber industry provides builders with standards for the strength of a given dimension of lumber. From these standards, builders can calculate how many feet a floor joist can span from one support to another.

typically constructed of lumber, although, with the fluctuation in lumber supplies and costs, some builders are now experimenting with panelization, steel framing, structural insulated panels, and other structural system options. We're going to address conventional lumber framing; it's still the industry standard.

Long before construction begins, your builder and architect will have engineered the frame structure based on the conceptual design of your home. Frame engineering takes into account many factors, both technical and cosmetic, and can be quite the science—especially when dealing with complex home designs that feature fewer walls and more open areas.

But no matter what the style of your home, architects and engineers must carefully design every inch of the walls, floors, and ceilings. The deflection and load-bearing capacities of each structural member are precisely calculated and engineered to support the stresses and weights of the home and its contents. What this means is that any time the builder makes even the smallest alteration in the frame, such as moving a window or door, the engineering of the frame design itself is affected. Even simple changes may require alterations to dozens of components of the original frame in order to protect its strength and integrity. In other words, once you've finished the design phase of your home, even a little change is a big change.

Once the planning is done, your builder will order all the necessary materials and lumber to construct the frame. An experienced homebuilder will usually have a team of estimators who are able to accurately calculate the exact amount of each material necessary for all phases of construction, leaving little surplus and saving you money. Since builders can choose from many grades and types of materials these days, they have to decide which materials are most appropriate for your new home. Just remember: you get what you pay for.

No matter what materials your builder decided to use, framing your home is not really a single task, but five: the floor system; the first floor wall framing; the second floor frame; the trusses; and the exterior trim. Your builder should coordinate the delivery of materials for each task to correspond with its completion; there's no sense in letting building materials sit around your homesite where you could experience losses due to theft or weather damage.

Now let's take a closer look at the framing process.

The Floor System

If your home is built on a slab foundation, you can skip this section: you don't need to build a floor system, because your concrete slab itself serves as the actual floor. However, if your home is being built on either a basement or crawlspace foundation, it becomes necessary to construct a floor system.

Generally speaking, there are three steps in the floor system construction: floor joists, bridging, and subfloor. Let's look at each.

Framers lay out the floor system, which can be dimensional lumber, open web, or I-like joists.

Floor joists. The most common type of flooring system uses floor joists. A floor joist system is a series of supports laid on edge horizontally. These supports run the length or width of the home, creating a base for the subfloor panels.

Many times, the distance between basement walls is too great for normal lumber joists to span. When this situation occurs, your builder may use reinforced steel I-beams in conjunction with typical lumber joists to reinforce the normal lumber joist system. The steel I-beams are capable of spanning a much greater distance and can support much more weight than lumber joists.

Still need more flooring support? Your builder may also insert supporting columns in the basement under the main floor; however, overuse of supporting columns can result in basement floor space with less appeal and fewer options for design and recreation. Your builder should carefully consider the placement of each support to maximize the basement's contiguous areas.

Today, builders have three basic choices for flooring systems: dimensional lumber joist

Open web joists

I-like joists

Cross bracing ties the flooring
members together making the
floor more rigid.

systems, open-web joists, and I-like joists. Let's take a brief look at each.

Dimensional lumber joist systems have been around for a long time. These are onsite, stick-built systems that are cut to fit.

Open web systems are pre-engineered, like truss systems for the roof. Unlike solid dimensional lumber joists, these systems use crisscrossing members that create open spaces that make it easier to work with the mechanical systems in your home—the ductwork, plumbing, and electrical systems.

I-like joists are also pre-engineered systems. I-like joists look like steel I-beams; they're made of solid wood flanges on either end, with thinner, oriented strand board (OSB) "webs." These I-like joists save on lumber and are easy to work with, since punching out holes in the thinner material is easier than drilling through solid lumber. I-like joists are also strong and straight and are available in lengths up to 60 feet, which makes them ideal for spanning long distances.

What should your builder use? It depends on the home. All of these systems have advantages. But for practicality and environmental friendliness, open webs and I-joists continue to grow in popularity. It's also not unusual for your builder to combine some or all of these flooring systems in a single home.

Bridging or cross-bracing

The next step in constructing the flooring system is stabilizing the floor joists using a technique called bridging, sometimes called cross-bracing. Bridging consists of placing diagonal supports between each floor joist, thus tying together all the joists in a series. By using bridging, the builder can minimize the independent movement, or "trampoline effect," of each joist...and much of that annoying floor squeaking that happens when joists are permitted to move separately. Bridging or lateral bracing of the floor joists is done on both the first- and second-level floors of the home. This bridging is called cross-bracing when it's used in an open web floor system.

Subfloor

Once the floor joists are in place, your builder is ready to install the subfloor, which is the surface placed directly on the floor joists that provides a base on which to build the interior and exterior walls of the frame. For the subfloor, your builder will probably use either

LP TopNotch® Oriented Strand Board (OSB) Panels · www.lpcorp.com

OSB is an innovative, affordable, and environmentally smart wood-based product—and LP produces more OSB—six billion feet a year—than any other home building products manufacturer in the world.

The innovative Top Notch OSB panels offer a patented vertical notching system in the tongue and panel ends; they also have self-spacing tongue-and-groove edges for easy installation and a uniform, level surface. Top Notch panels are further engineered using flake geometry, so that the surface layers are perpendicular to the core layers, increasing strength and durability. It's also protected by a transferable, 20-year warranty.

Once the subfloor is completed, the walls are laid out per the blueprints and assembled. Custom stick framing allows the framers to "measure twice and cut once," making adjustments where necessary for the foundation.

tongue-and-groove oriented strand board or plywood. Oriented strand board (OSB, as it is often referred to in the industry) is usually preferred because of its superior strength and resistance to warping. Boards cut in tongue-and-groove fashion fit together in interlocking channels at the seams, which helps provide a level, almost seamless, surface for the floor (see *Product Spotlight*).

The 4' x 8' sheets of subfloor are usually attached to the joists using a combination of screws, nails, and glue. By screwing or using ring shank nails and gluing the subfloor to the joists, your builder can provide a solid, stable floor and reduce squeaking, warping, shifting, and bowing. A smooth subfloor surface free of defects is important because it's the surface to which the final flooring product (carpet, laminate, wood plank, sheet vinyl, ceramic tile, etc.) will directly adhere. On a slab foundation, the final flooring will be applied directly over the concrete slab surface.

That's it for the flooring system. Now it's time to move on to framing the walls.

Once the floor joists are in place a construction-grade glue is applied to the top of the floor joists. Then the subfloor is quickly put in place.

Some builders build non-load-bearing walls with studs only 24 inches on-center. Why? It's less expensive. But this cost-cutting measure can result in a "wavy" wall surface...which may be fine if you're a surfer, but probably not what you want for the interior walls of your home. We prefer to place studs 16 inches on center, which provides more nailing surface when hanging drywall, thus helping to prevent wavy walls.

So beware. A builder can save from 50 to 100 2x4s by going to 24 inches on center. That's only a few hundred dollars in material costs. But the impact to your home can be significant. And if a builder is cutting back on 2x4s, you have to ask: where else might he or she be cutting?

The sill sealer is installed before setting the wall in place. The sill sealer protects the wood from the concrete and reduces air infiltration.

Wall Framing

You've probably heard the rule "measure twice, cut once." It's great advice—and nowhere is it more important than in wall framing. That's why the framing crew does a lot of work with a tape measure and a pencil before the walls actually start going up.

First, the framers will make a chalk line to mark the location of all walls on the subfloor. Next, they position the bottom plate (horizontal boards of the wall section) on the floor and mark where each vertical 2x4 stud will attach. Then the framers will arrange the studs on the plates and nail the system together as it lies on the floor. Studs are typically positioned every 16 inches along a wall section. In the industry, this technique is referred to as "16 inches on center," meaning the centers of each stud are 16 inches apart.

At the time of wall framing, the carpenters will make openings in the stud construction to accommodate windows and doors. Also, if you have an oversized bathtub or shower units being installed in the home, the carpenters may need to construct mounting or support frames for them at this time. This allows these units to actually be installed at this phase of construction, when maneuverability is not yet hindered by finished interior walls and doors.

Custom-built walls are hoisted over the anchor bolts and placed on the sill sealer.

The corners and some two-story walls should be braced with additional structural material. In this case, a material sturdier than the foam sheathing reinforces the corner and the two-story wall.

Once the tubs and showers are installed, a plastic cover is usually placed inside them to help protect them from damage.

As multiple sections of the first floor exterior walls are completed, the framers stand them up, brace them temporarily, and fasten them to the anchor bolts through the sill plate. It's important that your builder apply foam insulation under the bottom plate at the foundation. Doing so can drastically reduce air leakage and improve the home's heating and cooling efficiency.

Where the walls join to make corners, the carpenters will nail in corner braces: either wood panels or metal strips that run diagonally from top to bottom near the corners of each wall. These braces restrict lateral movement of the frame and help preserve its squareness.

Conscientious builders may use a special bracing product—a thin reinforcing material—on the outside corners of the home. This material is only 1/8-inch thick, but is extremely strong, which allows your builder to put a sheathing product over the bracing. Adding sheathing over bracing makes it easier to insulate and prevent air infiltration (see *Product Spotlight*).

Hmm. Must be time to talk about sheathing.

⚒ Hard Hat Area:

Some builders use metal straps or tie-downs instead of anchor bolts, but these have a tendency to allow some movement in the frame. These tie-downs are not unlike the twist ties you use to reseal your plastic bag of bagels—not exactly the most secure method of securing the frame of your home to the foundation.

Owens Corning ProPink sheathing is an excellent insulator and water barrier. The sheathing is secured with capped nails and the seams and any damaged areas are taped to reduce air infiltration.

Sheathing

Once the wall frame is erected, it's time for the framers to apply sheets of sheathing to the exterior walls. The sheathing both reinforces the wall and provides an initial layer of insulation for the home.

Sheathing is attached to the exterior walls of the frame using a collared, or capped, nail. The ends of these nails are fitted with collars that prevent them from pulling through the sheathing when they're subjected to natural stresses. The edges of the sheathing fit together in a tongue-and-groove fashion, then are sealed with a special sheathing tape to minimize air infiltration.

Builders use a variety of sheathing materials to cover the exterior of a house's frame, ranging from common foil-faced materials to the high-tech extruded polystyrene board, such as OwensCorning's PROPINK insulated sheathing (see *Product Spotlight*). Beware of plywood sheathing: it can lead to mold problems.

Now that the walls are in place, the home is ready for its ceiling and roof systems.

Owens Corning ProPink sheathing fits together in a tongue and groove fashion. The seams are fastened with capped nails and then taped to achieve an insulation and air infiltration barrier.

⭐ Product Spotlight: The top building products on the market today.

Owens Corning Sheathing • www.owenscorning.com

Owens Corning is one of America's premier manufacturers of building materials...and their PROPINK® insulating sheathing is one of the industry's premium insulating panels. It features a tough plastic laminated skin on both sides of its rigid foam core, which makes it extremely resistant to both construction damage and possible water infiltration. So it's an ideal choice for new construction.

Exterior walls made of PROPINK deliver considerably greater R-value than plywood, oriented strand board (OSB) or other foil-faced insulation products (which are also more susceptible to water damage); in fact, once fiberglass insulation is placed in the exterior wall stud cavities, the completed wall can achieve a total value of R-20.

PROPINK is designed to be used with either wood or metal studs and suits a variety of exterior finishes including wood siding, vinyl, metal and aluminum sidings; masonry veneer; and reinforced stucco.

OWENS CORNING ®

INNOVATIONS FOR LIVING™

Today's truss designs can be engineered for vaulted, sloped, and stepped ceilings.

Rafters are custom site built and very costly because of the larger dimensional lumber required and the length of time it takes to build these roof systems. Rafter systems can take two weeks to frame.

⌐ On The Level:

The walls of the home are usually constructed of standard or finger-jointed 2x4 lumber. If the weather cooperates, an experienced framing crew working together systematically can complete the wall framing in five to ten days.

Why, then, are modular homes constructed with 2x6 lumber? Because they have to withstand the shocks and shaking of highway travel. Some extremely energy-conscious builders will use 2x6s, too, but the value of this strategy is very debatable.

Roof Systems

The roof system is primarily made up of lumber triangles that create the attic space and serve as the foundation for the shingles. This system can be put together in two different ways. The triangles can be stick built onsite, to create what are called "rafters." Or they can be built in a factory, in which case they're called "trusses."

Most builders prefer to use trusses in lieu of a stick-built rafter system. Why?

For a number of good reasons. Rafters, which are built onsite, are larger and more expensive to build due to their labor requirements. They require measuring and cutting lumber onsite, so there's waste to deal with. And building rafters is time consuming. The whole job of building rafters can take a week or two.

Trusses are usually set using a crane. The entire truss package can usually be set in one day.

After the trusses are in place, the framers install the roof decking.

The roof decking needs some room to expand and contract. "H" clips are used for proper spacing and to help stabilize the seams.

The framers install a felt-type paper to help keep rain out of the structure until the roofer can install the shingles and complete the roof system.

On the other hand, consider truss systems:

- Trusses are precisely engineered, efficiently and conveniently forming the ceiling and the roof at the same time. It's an environmentally friendly approach, since it requires less lumber.
- Wood trusses are engineered to span the distance between the outside walls of the house. Since the trusses bear weight primarily on the exterior walls, the builder has greater flexibility with the interior walls and house floor plan.
- The truss system can be installed in significantly less time than rafters. A couple of workers with a crane can install the truss system in a day or less. While they cost more per piece they save much more in labor costs.

Even when pre-engineered trusses are used, the carpenters may still build rafters onsite for such items as front porches, three-car garages, dormer windows, screened porches, and other irregularities in the roof line.

Once the trusses are in place, 4'x 8' sheets of roof decking are nailed to the exterior plane of the trusses, forming the actual roof. The roof decking, usually 7/16-inch oriented strand board, is secured in place by the framers with nails and ply-clips, which are H-shaped aluminum clips that properly space the decking and hold the roof decking together between each truss. This extra precaution minimizes ridging, or "wavy" roofs, and allows the OSB to expand and contract.

The final step for the framing crew is to install a layer of protective felt tar paper over the bare roof decking. The tar paper is required under all fiberglass shingles and serves to temporarily protect the roof decking from rain and snow until the roofers are able to apply the permanent roofing material. It's also an added layer of moisture protection against wind-driven rain that might be forced up under the shingles.

¢ Our Two Cents:

As you might imagine, lots of builders live in big homes they've built for themselves. Some builders just can't quit building. They live in one place for a few years, then decide they have to build themselves something new. It's in their blood. It's what they do.

But regardless of how or where your builder lives, here's a fundamental question: is your builder building you a home that the builder would live in? That is, would your builder feel confident living in your new home? Was your home truly created to be durable and comfortable and energy efficient and attractive?

It's not a silly question. Don't be afraid to ask it.

High-quality windows such as Andersen Windows 200 Series add value and comfort to a home. Taping the flanges of the windows offers another layer of water and air infiltration protection.

The windows and doors are delivered during the final stages of framing to minimize theft and damage.

☑ EXTERIOR DOORS AND WINDOWS

The Ins and Outs Of Building Your Home

After the framing and roof systems have been completed, your builder can have the windows and exterior doors delivered to the homesite and installed. You may have been drawn to the windows and exterior doors in your new home because of their beauty. But they're also critical to your home's energy efficiency. A smart builder will help you understand all the roles the windows and doors play—beyond opening, closing, and cleaning.

Windows

Your builder can choose from literally hundreds of window types, styles, and brands when building your home. And while you'll probably want as many windows as possible on the front and back of the house, you'll want to balance your desire for natural light and an open view with the logistical constraints of the structure itself. For example, your builder has

✖ Hard Hat Area:

A conscientious builder will rarely use aluminum windows because they are such poor insulators. Extreme differences in temperature and humidity inside and outside a home offer proof: if you've ever had small puddles of water below your windows that result from the aluminum windows "sweating," or had frost you can scrape from the frame in winter, you know what we mean.

On The Level:

Once the framing is complete, your builder should perform a level check on the framing to be sure that it's vertical and square by holding a level across the framing studs to detect any bowing or misplacement. The builder or construction manager should check every area of the framing against the blueprints, double-checking proper structure, quality, and adherence to building codes. It's not uncommon for an exacting builder to mark any imperfection in the frame with a brightly colored spray paint so that the framers know where to make corrections and adjustments. In our experience, this review is critical; even the best framing crews can make mistakes.

to think about the strength and insulation value of the walls as well as the curb appeal of the home. These values are affected by the number, type, and style of window used.

Types of windows available include stationary, or "picture" windows; transom windows; horizontal sliding windows; double- and single-hung sash windows; and a wide variety of other specialty windows, each designed to fit a different space or create a different effect. Many window makers, including Andersen Corporation, make a wide range of window types, giving your builder a great selection at a dependable level of quality (see *Product Spotlight*).

The most common type of window used on homes today is the double-hung sash window. Double-hung windows consist of two frames of glass, or sashes, positioned in a vertically stacked fashion. The two sashes can slide up or down along a track to open or close the window. The frames on most modern double-hung windows are also capable of being tilted into the house or removed altogether, which allows for easier cleaning or other maintenance—especially on the second floor, since it eliminates the need for cumbersome extension ladders.

Today, windows are manufactured offsite and are sold to the builder as pre-assembled units that can be inserted directly into the opening in the wall frame. The window sash is typically made of wood, aluminum, or vinyl.

Many builders prefer to use wood windows because of their advantages over those constructed with other materials:

- Wood is a better insulator than either vinyl or aluminum.
- Wood can be painted, giving the homeowner flexibility to stain or paint the windows to match the decor or color schemes for the home.

A very popular window used in home construction today is a vinyl-clad, wood window that is double paned with a thermally insulated vacuum barrier between each pane, giving the window an excellent insulation value. Some windows feature a decorative muntin, or divider, enclosed between the two panes of glass. Homeowners appreciate the enclosed muntins as opposed to true divided panes of glass because they are protected from damage and dust. Also, having a continuous glass surface makes window cleaning considerably easier.

When cost is of special concern, builders may opt for a vinyl-based window. Some of today's vinyl windows offer many designs, but at a much lower cost. Vinyl offers a compromise between the superior insulation value and craftsmanship of wood windows and the affordability of aluminum windows. A disadvantage of the vinyl window is that you can't paint it, and the number of color choices is limited.

Speaking of cost, it's a great idea when comparing builders (especially production builders) to count the windows that go into their homes. Good windows cost about $400

Andersen Windows · www.andersenwindows.com

For more than 100 years, Andersen Corporation has been the name most Americans associate with beautiful, energy-efficient windows. And for good reason: Andersen makes some of the industry's best wood and vinyl-clad wood windows. The company manufactures a complete line of windows and doors to fit the style of virtually any home you're building.

Andersen® 400 Series tilt-wash double-hung windows give homes the beauty of natural wood interiors, combined with weather-tight performance and a long-lasting, low-maintenance vinyl exterior. The unique tilt-wash system makes cleaning these windows a breeze.

apiece, and the number of windows production builders use can vary wildly. The point is, a home that seems like a "bargain" may actually be skimping on the very items, such as windows, that make the home a nicer place to live.

After the window jamb is set in place, the framers need to make certain it's completely level. They may make adjustments using shims, or small wedges of wood, to make sure the window fits squarely. The window is nailed to the framing studs and later, during the interior trim stage of the home, decorative trim and moldings can be placed around the casing.

Exterior doors

Once your builder has installed the windows, the next step is to install the exterior doors. Like windows, doors are available in lots of sizes, styles, and types. As with window selections, the home design largely dictates the style and type of doors used.

For added insulation and durability, most builders use insulated steel or fiberglass exterior doors. These doors are usually made with embossed panels, and sometimes windows, to add depth and character. With the paint and stain technologies available today, these doors can easily be made to look like natural wood doors, if that's your preference.

So why not use a real wood door? Because unlike a wooden frame that holds glass for a window and is opened only occasionally, an exterior wooden door must efficiently seal an opening that will be opened and closed constantly. When exposed to constantly changing weather conditions, a large piece of wood may expand or contract slightly, affecting its ability to seal and insulate the house. Additionally, wooden doors, by constant use, show more wear

Continuous soffit venting is cut into the SmartTrim Soffit material. The continuous vent allows the attic area to most effectively exchange air.

and require more maintenance than fiberglass or metal doors.

As for your garage door, more and more builders are using a metal overhead garage door with embossed panels instead of the heavier, more maintenance-prone wood garage doors. Metal overhead doors won't warp like wood doors, require less frequent painting, and are lighter and easier to open.

Now that the framing crew has erected the floor, wall, and roof systems, the home's basic framework has been established, and you have your first real view of the shape and size of your new home. Your builder can now begin to add the other materials that will to protect your home from the elements.

☑ EXTERIOR TRIM

Trimming Up The Outside

Before the siding is installed, the framers will begin preliminary work on the exterior trim stage of construction. Exterior trim is the material used to finish the outside of the home around the windows, porch posts, soffit, doors— basically, anywhere where there's a corner or change of direction in the surface or where differing materials meet (e.g., where brick meets the vinyl siding on the side of a home). For many years, builders have used a rough-sawn and textured spruce or cedar wood for exterior trim work. Using a rough-textured trim board was a benefit to the homeowner because the roughness helped hide the natural imperfections in the wood and helped the wood take stain and paint more readily. Today, more builders are also using products such as LP SmartSide trim, which combines engineered wood with all the beauty of solid wood and offers greater durability (see *Product Spotlight*).

At this point, the framers will also build the soffit. Your home's trusses hang over the exterior walls to allow for water runoff. The soffit is the bottom of the overhang that runs from the end of the truss and to the wall. Building codes usually require venting to be placed in the soffit to aid in attic ventilation. The most effective method for providing ventilation to the attic is a continuous soffit vent. As its name suggests, this vent is a single, long vent running the entire length of the soffit. (Many builders, attempting to cut costs, will use smaller, intermittent soffit vents, which are not nearly as effective.)

When combined with ridge venting on the roof (described later in this chapter), a continuous soffit vent lets more air flow through the attic, which most effectively allows hot air to escape and prevents moisture and condensation from forming.

ROOFING

Putting A Lid On It

The next stage of construction is to protect your home's roof with some type of permanent covering. The choice of covering is usually determined by the region's climate, the budget, and the homeowner's preference. While the variety of roof coverings available ranges from terracotta and slate tile to metal panels and tar roofs, the vast majority of builders use asphalt roofing shingles.

Roofing: Shingles

The first step in the roofing process is to measure the correct spacing between rows of shingles and to mark the exact position of each row with a chalk line. Using the chalk lines as guides, the roofers will nail into place each row of shingles, starting at the bottom and working their way to the ridge, or top, of the roof. Subsequent rows of shingles overlap each other to form double or triple layers over the entire roof surface. You'll want to make sure your builder is using a good shingle from Owens Corning or some other reputable manufacturer (see *Product Spotlight*).

It must be time to roof the house because the roofing materials were delivered 'just in time.'

The roofer nails a row of shingles in place, then overlaps and staggers subsequent rows up to the peak of the roof.

After the roofer chalks out guidelines a starter course is set in place. The starter course is a shingle cut in half and reversed so that the seal strip is at the windward edge.

The roofer installs flashing to make the union between the chase and the shingles more water infiltration resistant.

Some elements of your home's roof design require special attention to ensure that your home stays dry. For example, when two roof lines meet to form a valley, special care must be taken to use valley roll, which adds reinforcement and provides an additional water barrier at this collection point. A lot of water will be passing through this valley. (Incidentally, if you ever get on the roof, be careful not to step in the valleys. You can tear the valley roll material under the shingles.)

When a roof runs into a wall or fireplace chase, a sheet of metal called flashing is often used. Flashing can be aluminum, copper or even galvanized steel. It's laid and positioned as an additional flooring or protection under the shingles at these intersections of roof. Flashing is a tricky process that must be performed by professional roofers. They use the aforementioned metal product and

The roofer also installs the continuous ridge vent at the peak of the roof. This vent is caulked and nailed into place.

special sealants in an attempt to blend two surfaces into a single, waterproof seam—not an easy task at all! In fact, most roof leaks are due to incorrect installation of flashing. That's why it's so important to take care here. And it's important to understand that roofs do leak. Heck, when you think about it, boats leak, too, even though they're built to sit in the water, day in and day out. That's why boats have bilge pumps—and why you wouldn't want to be out to sea on a boat without one.

Roofing: Attic vents

Builders are required by building codes to install attic vents. The purpose of the attic vent is to allow hot air to escape from the attic during the summer and to prevent moisture from accumulating in the winter. Why? Well, reducing the temperature of the attic in the summer helps reduce cooling costs and also helps prolong the life of the shingles by reducing the temperature on the roof. Preventing moisture and condensation from forming during the colder seasons helps preserve the lumber and insulation in the attic from decay.

Some builders use 'pod' venting which is located a couple of feet down from the ridge and is not as effective as ridge venting.

Pod venting and other penetrations can clutter the back roof of a home. The home should look good on all sides not just the front.

Owens Corning Shingles • www.owenscorning.com

Owens Corning's Supreme® shingle is a great choice for a wide range of home styles. The Supreme is a three-tab shingle constructed with a fiberglass mat with durable and colorful granules. Because these shingles are coated with weathering-grade asphalt, they provide protection from harsh weather.

By the way: Owens Corning makes a wide variety of styles and colors of asphalt shingles. Consider the shingle color that will look best with the rest of your home's exterior appearance. You should also check with your homeowners' association to see if it specifies a particular shingle color or type for homes in your community before you make your decision. Based on what you find out, you might also want to consider an Oakridge Pro Series dimensional shingle for added interest and appeal.

OWENS CORNING ®

INNOVATIONS FOR LIVING™

Many builders use "pod" vents to ventilate the attic region. Pod vents are the small protrusions you see on some roofs positioned just below the ridge line; sometimes, they look like turtles marching across the roof. A more effective way to ventilate the attic is ridge venting: a system in which vents are positioned at the very peak of the ridge and span nearly the entire length of the ridge. This is not only more attractive, but more effective: since warm air rises, positioning the ridge vent at the highest point of the roof allows more hot air to escape.

☑ OUTSIDE APPEARANCES

Your Exterior Beauty Treatment

Sure, it was exciting to see your home's skeleton. But now it's time to hang some skin on the bones. Your siding, roof covering, exterior trim, and other elements really start to define your home's outside appearance. Now it's time to start making it beautiful.

Homebuilders use a wide array of materials for siding and trim, ranging from traditional brick and wood to aluminum and vinyl siding, stucco, and wood shingles. All have their places, but we're going to focus on the more traditional materials.

Siding

The siding is the material used on the exterior of the home to cover the bare sheathing and to form a final protective surface. Since the siding is one of the primary elements in the appearance of your home, it's important for you and your builder to carefully consider the type and style of material used.

Wood siding

Select Canadian cedar is one common type of wood siding. Wood siding is nailed directly to the framing studs through the sheathing, and can be painted, stained, or even left to weather naturally.

The main problem with this or any wood siding is its vulnerability to the elements. If not properly maintained, wood can rot and sustain damage from water, UV rays, and salt spray. Additionally, wood can be attacked by ants, termites, and even woodpeckers. (Yes, woodpeckers. Ask someone who's had one: they can be terribly destructive. And the noise is not pleasant, either.)

With the windows and doors in place, the framers begin applying the siding. Today's popular siding choices are Hardi-plank cement board, vinyl siding, and brick.

Cement board siding

This relatively new material can be a great alternative to wood. A product such as James Hardie's Hardiplank® is a fiber-reinforced cement board siding that offers the beauty of wood without the maintenance hassles. It won't rot or crack and is more resistant to insects, fire, rain, and hail damage. More and more builders are using this product for its durability, longevity and lower maintenance.

Vinyl siding

As with many parts of the construction process, vinyl is a "happy medium" material choice. Low maintenance, affordability, practicality, and resale value are all reasons many builders today are using some sort of vinyl siding. Vinyl siding comes in a multitude of colors and is typically designed to simulate a wood grain texture. Let the buyer beware, though: many different grades and qualities of vinyl are available. Vinyl siding is usually measured in mil thickness—like trash bags. The higher the mil, the better the product will perform. You probably want siding that's at least 42 mil.

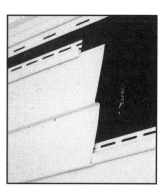

Sidings go on the home much like shingles, from the bottom up and usually overlapping or interlocking. Vinyl siding should not be nailed tight, but should actually float away from the sheathing slightly, allowing for expansion and contraction.

Masonry siding (brick, stone, and stucco)

It is hard to find a homeowner or builder today who doesn't appreciate the substantial and hardy character a masonry finish provides a home. However, brick is one of the most expensive siding materials available and, therefore, is used only sparingly on moderately-priced homes. Brick is also heavy; a home with brick siding requires a specially-designed foundation to support the load. For these reasons, many homes are built with a subtle balance of brick and plank siding.

There are many variations of brick styles and colors. Most bricks are clay-based and retain a hue of red. However, it is common for the brick manufacturer to add coloring and texturing agents to the clay before firing to achieve various cosmetic effects.

After the brick work is put up, it should be allowed to set for a few days. The bricklayers then return to clean the brick of mortar stains using a mild acid mixture, brushes, and long-handled extensions. After the acid washing, the brick is sprayed clean with water.

A masonry crew works as a team to build scaffolding, mix mortar, and move and lay bricks. Brick is costly because it is very labor intensive.

Exterior painting

Once exterior siding and trim work are finished, your builder can begin painting and finishing the exterior.

On the exterior of the home, builders use acrylic paint on all trim work and wood siding products. Acrylic paints have a number of advantages over oil-based or latex paints. Acrylic paints:

- Resist mold and mildew
- Hold the color longer
- Are more durable to weather conditions
- Have a satin sheen that sheds dirt more easily

Most exterior sidings, trim, and other pieces are air-sprayed for both the first, or prime coat, and second coat. Exceptions to this would be those materials that come pre-primed. In the case of pre-primed materials, only a final coat is applied by the painters. The equipment and talent used in spray painting have developed to a level of quality that results in even

Porter Paints · www.porterpaints.com

Porter has been making paints that have been preferred by builders, contractors, and homeowners for more than 80 years. Porter starts with superior raw materials, advanced formulations, state-of-the-art manufacturing processes, and higher levels of quality pigments, binders, and additives like INTERSEPT®—and less water and thinners—than many other paint companies. As a result, Porter paints are easier to apply, easy to wash, and extremely durable.

Painters spray a finish coat of Porter Paint over a factory primed piece of SmartTrim. The initial paint job on your home should last 3-4 years. Subsequent paint applications last longer.

coverage, eliminating brush marks and covering other imperfections in the wood. You'll also want to pay attention to the paint your builder is using; Porter Paints, for example, is a great choice. You don't want to use a cheap paint to protect your most valuable investment. In addition, most conscientious builders will offer at least a dozen exterior paint colors to allow you to personalize your home (see *Product Spotlight*).

In all cases, you should plan on repainting your home within the first three or four years. Subsequent repaintings can then occur about every five to eight years, depending on climate, color, and other factors.

Porch columns, railings, and other ornate trim pieces are often painted with a brush because of their intricate designs. These trim and accent pieces are often made from cedar, so an oil-based primer is used due to its effectiveness in holding back or sealing the tannin "bleeding" that happens naturally with this type of wood. If your builder is using the SmartSide trim we mentioned earlier, these bleeding problems are eliminated and latex paint can be used.

Homes with vinyl siding require only the trim to be painted, as the vinyl comes pre-colored. This also means that vinyl siding saves you time and maintenance worries, since it never needs to be painted.

Exterior painting consists of spraying the large wall surfaces and a lot of brush painting of the smaller, more intricate trim areas.

Start		Month 2	Month 3	Month 4	Month 5	Finish

Your home begins to look like a house.

Oil or acrylic? Acrylic or oil? Which sort of exterior paint should your builder use for your home and does it really matter? Well, yes and no.

Builders used to favor oil-based paints exclusively because of their durability.

Today, however, latex paints have advanced to the point where they really are as durable as oil-based paints. They're also easier to work with and far more environmentally friendly.

In many cases, builders will use latex paints as long as weather permits. If your home is being painted during a cold-weather month, your builder may use an oil-based paint.

Does it matter? It matters only that you know whether your home was painted with oil or latex, so you can use the right paint when it's time for touch-ups. In most cases, your builder will leave you a can of paint for just this reason.

Caulking serves both aesthetic and functional purposes. It joins surfaces and helps reduce water and air infiltration.

Exterior Caulking

After the home has been sided and painted, the exterior caulking is applied. A water and weatherproof caulking compound, usually silicone based, is applied around all doors, windows, wood joints, soffit areas, and almost anywhere dissimilar materials meet. Caulking prevents water and air infiltration and enhances the home's insulation R-value. Builders prefer a caulking that is premixed with color pigment to better match the color of the exterior paint. The caulking process generally takes four or five hours to complete.

Gutters and Downspouts

Gutters and downspouts are installed on the fascia board (the front piece of trim that runs just under the roof), just beneath the last row of shingles. Gutters are the horizontal troughs at the bottom of the roof surface used to catch water runoff. The gutters are installed using spikes and ferrules. A ferrule is the long tube that acts as a casing for the spike, which runs through the gutter and into the fascia board. (Some gutters are installed with screws.) The gutters are fitted with end caps and pitched with a slight slope for proper drainage. This allows them to channel water to the downspouts, which then carry the water down to the ground and onto an erosion-preventing splash block.

The width of the gutters used on your home is determined by the square footage of the roofing area; the larger the roofing area, the more water that will be running off it. Five-inch gutters and 2"x3" downspouts are used on most homes. Larger roof areas may need larger gutters and downspouts.

Gutters and downspouts are manufactured in both preformed sections and continuous seamless lengths. Continuous seamless gutters are formed from a roll of pre-pared aluminum through a specialized forming machine. They are ideal because the varying sections of the gutter are rolled out to the specified length and easily installed. These gutters are actually made onsite by gutter makers. The rolls of aluminum used to form the gutters are typically prepared with a colored enamel finish already baked on, saving the builder time—and the homeowner the expense and hassle of painting.

The custom length gutter is nailed to the gutter board using spikes and ferrule.

⟨$⟩ Our Two Cents:

It's an age-old question in the homebuilding industry: do you caulk before or after you paint? If you caulk before you paint the house, then you can paint the caulk and everything looks neat and uniform...but you can have trouble with the caulk. If you caulk with a good-quality caulk after you paint, the caulk will perform better...but it may not be quite as attractive.

Why? Because higher-quality caulks need time to cure. These caulks remain wetter and more pliable, allowing them to maintain a better seal between the expanding and contracting surfaces of your home. This "wetter" caulk can't be painted for three to six months. It can also collect dirt so that it discolors.

This is simply the nature of the beast. You can use a cheap caulk and paint it right away, but it won't expand and contract with your exterior surfaces and won't do a very good job for you. You can wait six months and paint a premium caulk. Or you can live with your discolored caulk until you repaint the entire house.

Your home begins to look like a house.

Most driveways and sidewalks should be poured with a minimum of 4000 PSI (pounds per square inch) concrete approximately four inches thick to assure proper strength. The concrete surface is treated with a cure-and-seal sealant that will lock in moisture and prolong the life of the concrete.

Technical note: many people confuse the terms "concrete" and "cement." This is actually like confusing "cake" and "flour." Cement is an ingredient that goes into making concrete.

Speaking of which... be sure you ask your builder about your concrete PSI. Some builders will try to cut corners by using less cement, which lowers the PSI and makes the concrete weaker. You can't tell by looking at it, so ask.

Exterior Concrete Work

Sometime after the completion of the foundation work and exterior painting, your builder will arrange for any necessary concrete work to be performed. Exterior concrete work includes driveways, sidewalks, and patios.

We put concrete work in this section of the book because it relates to the exterior appearance and functionality of the home; however, your builder may intentionally delay the pouring of exterior concrete areas to ensure that all trenching and digging have been done and that all buried cables, wires, and sewer and water lines have been properly installed.

Concrete is usually installed in multiple pours. The different concrete batches have slightly different colors which eventually even out in color.

Once your builder is ready to proceed, 2x4 forms are placed for your driveway, patio, porch, and sidewalk. The forms hold the concrete as it cures. Once the forms are constructed, the areas inside the forms are lined with a layer of sand to provide a firm base for the concrete. The concrete is then poured between the forms.

As the concrete begins to cure, the finishers draw a push broom across the surface to leave a rough-textured surface. The rough texture is desirable on exterior concrete areas because it provides improved traction. The final step is to apply a sealant to the concrete. You should reseal the driveway every year to extend its life—more on this later.

Now that the concrete is curing, it's a good time to stand back and take a good look at your new home. Enjoy the view. It's one of many "Kodak® moments" you'll have during the building process. But there's still a lot to do—in fact, a lot is already going on—inside the house. Electrical and plumbing work, cabinets, the heating and cooling system, and more are being installed. In addition, carpet, drywall, fixtures, molding, and more have been ordered and scheduled for completion.

Go ahead, snap a couple of pictures. Then let's head inside. We have a schedule to keep, you know.

What's Happening To Your Dream?

Right now, your new home is up and mostly covered. You may naturally be entering into that mental stage known by all of us as "Are we there yet?" The answer, as anyone who's taken a long drive with the kids knows, is, "We're almost there. Not too much longer." So let's recap where we are.

With all that we've discussed being done to the outside of the home to this point, remember that the builder began scheduling many activities that take place in the interior of the home once the basic physical structure of the home was erected. After the framing processes are completed, construction activity in and around the home increases drastically. This is why it's so critical for your homebuilder to have at least one full-time construction manager on the jobsite, managing, supervising, and orchestrating the many activities. With so many things being done simultaneously, care must be taken to maintain control over the job and prevent chaos. You don't want workers bumping into each other and becoming distracted and annoyed, which could affect the quality of their work.

Back in the framing stage of construction, well in advance of exterior painting, your builder should have met with you to review and confirm your initial selections of paint colors, as well as interior floor coverings, cabinet styles, appliance types, and other items. The experienced homebuilder also knows that homeowners have a tendency to change their minds. In order for your builder to accommodate your requests and still complete the home in a timely and efficient manner, any changes must be addressed as early as possible in the construction process. Remember, builders need to order materials and schedule craftsmen far in advance of the actual installation date in order to remain efficient.

Okay...break is over. Back to work. We're over halfway through your new home's construction. But we still have a lot of work to do.

CHAPTER SEVEN

Let's get rough with your home in order to make it more comfortable.

At this point, your new home is starting to look good. And when it's completed, you'll want your home to feel as good as it looks.

Maybe even better, actually. Some of us would take a comfortable home over an award-winning showplace any day...

In any case, it's the comfort of your home that your builder is focusing on at this stage of the construction process. After framing is finished, your builder must begin to prepare the house for the mechanical systems—heating and cooling systems, plumbing, and electrical systems—that will ultimately determine the level of comfort in your home.

We'll also discuss insulation in this chapter, as it plays a critical role in the energy efficiency of the mechanical systems, as well as in the overall efficiency of the home itself.

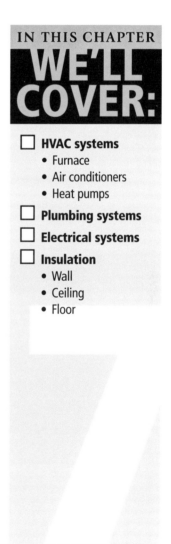

IN THIS CHAPTER

WE'LL COVER:

☐ **HVAC systems**
  • Furnace
  • Air conditioners
  • Heat pumps

☐ **Plumbing systems**

☐ **Electrical systems**

☐ **Insulation**
  • Wall
  • Ceiling
  • Floor

The mechanical systems are commonly referred to as "rough-ins." Why? Just take a look at your home before the drywall conceals the insulation and mechanical systems, and you'll get your answer. The sight of piping, ductwork, and wiring networking through your home's framework can look pretty complicated and unattractive at this point in construction. But attractiveness is not a goal at this point in the process. Drywall will eventually cover the walls and prevent easy access to electrical wiring, plumbing lines, ventilation ducts, and insulation. Establishing the proper infrastructure for each of these critical systems now assures you that the drywall won't have to be torn down later to make repairs or adjustments.

A well-built home and good name-brand heating and cooling equipment like Trane make a home comfortable. Some experts say that 40% of homes built today have comfort issues. (See Product Spotlight)

The HVAC contractor sets the furnace in place and installs a condensation drainage line to a required floor drain.

☑ HVAC SYSTEM

"HVAC!" (Gesundheit.)

We jest. Actually, the "HVAC" is not a sneeze, but rather an acronym for heating, ventilation, and air conditioning, and it's a common term in the building industry. Your HVAC system consists of all components involved in the distribution of heated or cooled air throughout the home. So, in reality, it might actually help *keep* you from sneezing.

The HVAC system includes:

- The furnace, air conditioner, or heat pump;
- The metal ductwork, or supply system;
- The cold air return system;
- Thermostats; and
- Venting for bathroom fans and clothes dryers.

Cinergy® Smart $aver® Program • www.cinergy.com

Many local utility companies believe so strongly in heat pumps that they offer special discounted rates (up to 15 percent) to customers who use a heat pump as their primary means of heating and cooling. For example, Cinergy/PSI, the electric utility serving many of the areas surrounding Indianapolis, offers the Smart $aver® program. If you're a Smart $aver homeowner, you receive a discounted heating rate because you use a high-efficiency heat pump. Check with Cinergy/PSI for details.

Cinergy Corporation was created in 1994 from the combination of The Cincinnati Gas & Electric Company and PSI Energy, Inc., the largest electric utility in Indiana. Based in Cincinnati, Ohio, Cinergy is today one of the leading diversified energy companies in the America, serving 1.5 million electric customers and about 500,000 gas customers in Indiana, Ohio, and Kentucky. Your local Cinergy representative will be happy to show you all the cost-saving advantages of a comfortable, high-efficiency electric heat pump.

Connecting multiple bath fan vents and exiting the roof in one location reduces leak-prone roof penetrations and reduces roof clutter.

Let's take a closer look at the components of your HVAC system and how they interrelate.

Ductwork, cold air returns, thermostats, and venting

We know, we know: these things seem less important than the actual mechanical equipment that's going to heat and cool your home. But we're going to talk about them first because your builder will probably install them first.

Your builder will hire a specialist to install the duct systems in the walls, floors, and ceilings and set the thermostat line in place. The ducts, generally made from sheet metal in round or rectangular sections—or, increasingly, today, a more flexible, insulated material—carry the warm or cold air into and out of the rooms in the house.

A builder concerned with the energy efficiency of the home should take special precautions to heavily insulate ducts that run through non-conditioned areas such as the attic. By insulating these ducts, the air inside is better able to retain its heat or coolness as it travels from the air handler or other conditioning units to each

The HVAC contractor custom builds the ductwork for each house. The quality of duct design and installation can have a big impact on the comfort of the home.

It is good practice for the HVAC installer to spray paint behind the cold air return grills to hide the unsightly workframe members.

room of the house. By insulating any duct traveling through a cold space, the builder minimizes the condensation that forms when warm air meets cold air.

Just to be clear: your supply ductwork brings heated or cooled air to the rooms of your home and distributes it through registers that are usually placed in the floor or the walls. The cold air return system sends air back to the conditioning systems where it's heated or cooled, as needed. The thermostat senses the temperature in your home and controls the operation of the HVAC system, turning it on and off as needed to achieve the temperatures you want.

Now that we've discussed how the air in your home is circulated, it's time to talk about how your air is conditioned—that is, heated and cooled. The most popular choices for homeowners today are an electric heat pump or a natural gas furnace combined with an electric air conditioner. Let's take a look at these options.

Heat pumps

The trend in home building today is to use a heat pump. While a furnace blows heated air in the winter and an air conditioner blows cooled air in the summer, the more modern heat pump efficiently serves the dual purpose of both heating and cooling.

Essentially, the heat pump is an energy-saving heating and cooling system that moves heat into and out of your home. In the summer, it's an extremely efficient air conditioner that works by moving unwanted heat from inside your home to the outside. In the winter, the heat pump reverses the process and absorbs heat from the outside air to bring it inside. A compressor motor concentrates the heat in a copper pipe and moves it to the inside furnace. This captured heat from the outside could be considered "free" heat; you pay only for the energy used to move it from the outside to the inside of your home.

The heat pumps of today are engineered with the latest technology to operate at an ultra-efficient level. When it's 47 degrees outside, a high-efficiency heat pump is 3.4 times more efficient than an electric furnace. Even when it's only 17 degrees outside, the energy-to-heat conversion ratio is 2.2. On average, for every dollar you spend on heat pump energy, you'll capture more than two dollars' worth of heat.

At most temperatures below 30 degrees, a total electric heat pump works in conjunction with an electric furnace. Although the heat pump is very efficient at lower temperatures, it

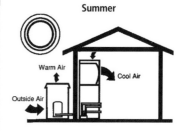

Heat Pump Cycle
Summer

Warm Air · Cool Air · Outside Air

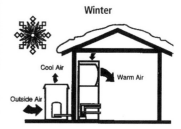

Winter

Cool Air · Warm Air · Outside Air

Heat pumps are really heat movers. Heat pumps work like a refrigerator and move heat from inside the home to the exterior during the summer time, then reverse this process during cooler months.

occasionally uses the furnace for extra heating capacity. Still, in many Midwestern cities, more than 90 percent of winter hours are over 22 degrees, so the backup furnace is needed only for a very small portion of your total heating requirement. To make the case for heat pumps as clear as possible, if you would ever mistakenly turn off your heat pump and rely on your furnace alone, your heating bills could easily double.

Heat pumps are clearly the most efficient way to heat and cool a home. So why do so many people misunderstand them?

Ask a roomful of a hundred people whether they like heat pumps, and you might well get only one or two affirmatives; in fact, lots of people would swear they'd never have a heat pump in their homes.

First, they're wrong. They all have heat pumps in their homes already. And so do you. Your refrigerator is a heat pump that works by taking the warm air inside the refrigerator and sending it out into your home, creating a cool interior for your milk and cheese.

Second, they're laboring under misconceptions. People who have had bad experiences with heat pumps in the past have probably been victims of poor home design and construction. With a properly insulated, energy-efficient home, a heat pump will heat and cool more uniformly, efficiently, and comfortably than your other options. And—PS—it costs less initially, too.

Furnace and air conditioner

Gas heat with an electric cooling system is another popular choice for heating and cooling your home. In this type of system, the air conditioner and the furnace share the same thermostat, ductwork and blower, acting like one system. Both pull air from the inside of the house, heat it or cool it, depending on your need, and send the reconditioned air back through the house.

As this stage of the construction process, your builder will call a plumber to run the gas lines to the furnace. However, even though all the ductwork is installed now, along with vent grills, registers, and other visible HVAC-related products, the actual heat pump or other furnace and air conditioner will be installed later on in the construction process, usually at the time of interior finishing. That's because you want this equipment where you can reach it—*not* hidden behind drywall. We'll briefly touch on installation in Chapter Eight.

PLUMBING SYSTEM

Water We Waiting For? Let's Do The Plumbing!

As you'll remember, we've already done at least a little plumbing in your new home; we've positioned the water service and supply lines just after we built your foundation. If you're building a home with a slab foundation, we've actually already done a fair amount of plumbing. But if your home is on a crawlspace or basement foundation, now's the time in the construction process that the internal supply lines are brought into the house.

From the initial supply lines under the main level floor, plumbers will install smaller supply lines that serve as the distribution network for the hot and cold water. These lines, typically 1/2-inch copper pipes, travel from the main supply lines and water heater to their final destinations—your sinks, showers, tubs, dishwasher, ice maker, washing machine, and the like.

You can think of the plumbing system as being made up of two smaller but equal systems, each having its own function. One half is the system of supply lines (water coming into the house), and the other half is the system of drain lines (water going out of the house). However you want to think of it, there are lots of pipes involved, and they all have to be installed somewhere within the framework of the house. The plumbers will be drilling holes through joists, studs, and the subflooring to accommodate the plumbing system. Local building codes detail specifications for the size, location, and number of these holes to assure the structural framework of your new house isn't compromised.

You might also remember that we set tubs and showers in place a while ago, due to their

⚙️ Our Two Cents:

It's too hot. It's too cold. It's too dry. It's too damp. How come you can spend so much money on systems to heat and cool your home and you still have problems—and arguments with your spouse—about indoor comfort?

Cool down. (Or warm up. Whatever.) Let's talk about it for a minute.

Sometimes, couples and families have legitimate differences of opinion about indoor temperature. Some like it hot, some like it not. But let's assume for a moment that we can all agree on what's comfortable inside your home.

The fact is, your HVAC system has been carefully designed and installed to do the job it's intended to do. Today more than ever, it's heating and cooling a home that's already pretty tight and energy efficient. Which means that the problem is probably not the equipment.

It's you.

Most comfort problems inside new homes are lifestyle related. Do you have lots of houseplants that have to be watered? When that water evaporates, where do you think it goes? What about that pot of boiling water that's cooking macaroni on your stove?

You might think burning candles in your home makes the place warm and inviting. But candles affect indoor air quality. They can give off small amounts of toxins such as acetone and benzene. (Don't be alarmed: normal candle use won't hurt you.) They can also leave dark shadows on your walls and soot from candle burning can invade your HVAC system.

And remember, since your home is really energy efficient, it's harder than ever for humidity and indoor pollutants to escape.

These are just a few examples of things you do that affect the air quality and comfort inside your home. So what do you do?

To much or too little moisture in the air can make you uncomfortable and can actually cause household damage. If you create a lot of moisture in your home, you might want to consider having a dehumidifier installed to help improve your comfort. If your home gets dry in the winter, consider the opposite: a humidifier that will help add moisture to the air. If you're concerned about indoor air quality, there are lots of air purifying options available.

As for temperature control, you can always experiment with rebalancing your system by opening and closing registers or redirecting air flow from your HVAC system with using the levels sometimes found on your ductwork. Try closing off the air flow to rooms you don't use, which will allow more conditioned air to flow to the rest of your home.

The best advice: learn how to control your thermostat (it's not difficult) and be aware of your activities that affect air quality. Your comfort systems are designed to work for you, especially if you're willing to do a little work with them.

Let's get rough with your home in order to make it more comfortable...

At any point where the plumbing lines penetrate the insulated envelope that separates non-conditioned areas, such as the attic and crawlspace, from living areas of the home, the gaps should be closed with a sealant. Not all builders will go to this amount of trouble. But this seemingly trivial detail prevents air infiltration and dramatically increases the energy efficiency of the home. This step may also be completed at the time of home insulation.

The plumbing contractor installs the supply and drain lines, water heater, tubs, and shower units during the rough-in stage. Also note in this picture the steel protector plates which protect the plumbing lines from the drywall nails.

size and weight; it was easy to set them in the home and frame around them rather than try to bring them in after the framing was done. (Some manufacturers do make sectionalized tub and shower units that can be carried in after framing.) The supply and drain pipes are usually installed to your tubs and showers at this time; however, the actual plumbing fixtures, such as faucets and showerheads, are installed later, when your home nears completion. These are things that can be scratched or damaged, so we don't want to put them in place until most of the heavy lifting and pounding is done.

One very important code requirement is the need to have any receptacles in the vicinity of a sink or water source operate on a ground fault interrupt (GFI) circuit. A GFI circuit is a safety precaution devised to interrupt the flow of electricity at the circuit the moment an appliance falters, or a short circuit develops.

You're probably familiar with GFIs; you have one on the plug end of your hair dryer. GFIs measure the flow of current between the wires in an appliance and prevent the flow of electricity between your appliance and an external ground—say, you, standing in a puddle of water on your bathroom floor. If the GFI detects a difference in the power flow, it automatically shuts off the flow of electricity, preventing you from getting a shock and maybe electrocuting yourself.

All electrical outlets that may come into contact with water—bathroom, kitchen, garage, and any outlets outside your home—should be protected by GFIs. This applies to you even if you decide to throw away this book and never build a new home. Bring your used home up to today's safety standards. The life you save may be your own.

A ground fault interrupt outlet (GFI) protects the outlet from faulty circuits. These outlets and circuits are safety devices placed near sinks, tubs, and exterior outlets.

☑ ELECTRICAL SYSTEM

A Powerful Next Step

The preliminary electrical work is usually performed after both the plumbing and HVAC systems have been installed. Why do things in this order? Because electrical wiring is flexible—much more flexible than big, bulky ductwork and rigid piping—so it can go over and around and between the components of other systems.

Your home's electrical system is more than a series of wires, outlets and switches. It's a complex series of electrical codes, standards, and plans, and the electricians that work on your home need to be familiar with all of it. At the preliminary electrical stage, electricians install the electrical wiring for all outlets, lighting, appliances, and utilities. Wiring comes in different sizes and types, depending on the electrical needs of the home; heat, light, entertainment, food preparation, security, and convenience all depend on receiving electricity the right way.

In addition, some builders today are also using what's known as *structured wiring*. Structured wiring is a way to organize the hundreds of feet of cable and wire that run through your home, and to bring television, video, audio, phone service, computer networking, Internet, security service, and more into multiple rooms of your home. Instead of running all these lines separately, builders can purchase products that combine these individual wires

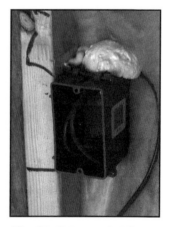

All outlets that are against the exterior wall should be sealed or foamed to reduce air infiltration.

After the electrical contractor marks each outlet, phone, cable, smoke detector, door bell, light switches, ceiling light, etc. , wires are run to each location.

and cables inside a single jacket. Services come into your home at a centralized service box, much like your breaker panel for your electric circuits. From here, they are distributed via high-performance structured wiring to multi-use outlets in every room of your home. Each room can be customized with outlets that meet your needs; you probably don't want Internet access in the bathroom, but you may want to see the TV.

After your home has been completely wired, the breaker box will be connected to an eight-foot metal grounding rod that has been placed into the ground outside. The actual breaker panel is not installed until the electrical finish step. Only two working breakers are installed at this time: one for the furnace to allow the heater to operate prior to electrical finish; and one for the temporary power outlet.

Circuit breakers, or breakers, monitor the electricity to all electrical circuits throughout your home and give you (or your electrician) the ability to control the flow of electricity to those circuits. When the demand for electricity on a particular circuit becomes excessive, the flow of electricity to that circuit is cut off automatically, or *broken*, by the breaker switch. You can reestablish the flow of electricity to that circuit by resetting the switch—lots easier than replacing fuses, as you may have had to do if you've ever owned an older home.

Once the temporary outlet is set up, the electrical rough-ins are almost done. The actual finished portions of the wiring, such as the receptacles, switches, and lights, are not installed until the electrical finish stage later in construction.

The electrical circuit wires are run to a circuit box or control panel usually located in the garage.

✔ PRELIMINARY INSPECTIONS

Keeping an Eye Out For Quality

If it seems to you that there's a lot going on at your new home right now, you're right. So how can you be sure everything's being done to the right specifications? After all, this is the last stage in your home's construction before the plumbing, electrical, and HVAC systems will be covered by drywall. If there's a problem, or something the builder needs to fix, now is the time to do it.

Onsite construction supervision significantly improves communications and the quality of the house under construction.

Remember those fees for those permits you had to pony up before your home actually started to be built? Here's where you get some of your money's worth. Each separate rough-in stage—HVAC, plumbing, and electrical—takes from two to five days to complete. Upon completion of all the rough-ins, it's usually required that your builder's work is approved by a local building inspector. The inspector checks for code violations in framing, plumbing, electrical wiring, and the HVAC system. Any violations found are noted onsite, and the builder is required to correct the violation before construction continues. These violations can be quite common; you'll often see them identified on your home with red tags. Don't worry. Red tags usually involve simple corrections, and construction can resume promptly. (If any major violations are found, the builder will typically have to pay a fine in order to have the home re-inspected.)

Because of the critical nature of this step in the construction process, a reputable builder will have numerous quality control checkpoints in place. A building inspector is no substitute for a good builder. If you've made the right builder decisions, these inspections shouldn't be much more than a formality.

Let's get rough with your home in order to make it more comfortable...

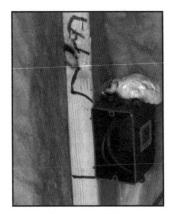

The insulation is carefully worked around all wiring and plumbing to envelop the home.

The insulation contractor places batt insulation in the wall cavity. Combining Owens Corning's ProPink and Owen's Corning batt wall insulation yields an R19.5 wall. (See Product Spotlight)

✓ INSULATION

Keeping Your Cool (And Warmth)

You've no doubt made a good decision regarding your new home's heating and cooling system. Now, to really reap the benefits of your system, your new home needs to be thoroughly insulated.

Insulation can be defined as a resistance to heat loss or gain. So it makes sense that insulation is rated in terms of its resistance factor, or "R-value." The higher the R-value of any insulation, the better it insulates.

What R-value should your new home have? In the Midwest, most local building codes mandate R-18 in side walls and R-30 in ceilings. Conservation-minded builders may surpass the recommended codes and insulate walls to R-19.5 and ceilings to R-38.

Many different materials can be used for insulation, but the material most commonly used for insulation is fiberglass. Fiberglass insulation is made from very fine fibers spun from

Owens Corning Insulation · www.owenscorning.com

Owens Corning is the name America trusts for a wide range of insulation products that reduce heating and cooling costs, reduce air infiltration, control moisture, and air ventilation in your home. The company manufactures PINK fiberglass batt insulation and loose fiberglass insulation for virtually every home insulation need. From attic to foundation, exterior walls to HVAC ductwork—even in interior walls for noise control—more homeowners and builders trust Owens Corning than any other brand.

The R-value of an average blanket thickness of Owens Corning unfaced insulation is R-13. This combined with the R-value of the previously installed sheathing, the vapor barrier, the drywall, and the exterior siding enables the walls to achieve an R-value of R-19.5.

OWENS CORNING ®

INNOVATIONS FOR LIVING™

glass and come in either batt blanket form or loose fiber form. The *batt form* comes either as faced (one side covered with a heavy paper) or unfaced flexible blankets sized to fit snugly between ceiling and floor joists or between wall studs. With faced batt, the paper acts as a vapor barrier, and can be stapled to studs and joists to keep the insulation in place. Unfaced batts are a little wider to fit inside studs without the need for stapling—but should have a vapor retarder installed over it if your builder uses them for your exterior walls. Unfaced insulation is also commonly used for attic floors, where a vapor retarder isn't necessary. The other type of insulation—the *loose fiber form* of fiberglass insulation—is sometimes preferred because subcontractors are able to use a special blower to disperse the insulation in hard-to-reach cavities such as attic spaces. Before putting up the batt

Ventilation spacers are placed from the soffit vents to the attic areas so that the insulation does not 'choke off' the air flow from the soffit to the ridge vents.

blankets (and a vapor retarder if using unfaced insulation), your builder injects a sealant into all cracks, seams, and holes around electrical outlets, between the slab and sill plate, and at any point where a wire or pipe enters the home from a non-insulated area. This process will minimize the amount of outside air infiltration and result in a more energy-efficient home.

How and when and what sort of insulation you install depends on the home and the

| Start | Month 1 | Month 2 | Month 3 | Month 4 | Month 5 | Finish |

stage of construction your home is in. While it's easy to fit batts between wall studs, it's tough to blow loose fiber insulation into the attic when there's no ceiling to hold it in place. Better to wait until after the drywall for this one. In other words, insulation is done partly before drywall and partly after. Let's take a closer look now.

Wall insulation

A batt insulation, faced or unfaced, is almost always used between the studs of the walls. There have been many new innovations in wall insulation but that innovation comes at a cost that doesn't yet justify the newer materials and additional labor. This section will describe the traditional batt insulation process.

As we've previously mentioned, any ductwork running through a non-conditioned airspace, such as the attic, should be wrapped with some type of insulating blanket. This helps the conditioned air inside the ducts retain its temperature as it's distributed throughout the home and prevents condensation when warm air inside the ductwork meets the cold attic air.

And, as long as we're in the attic, let's take a minute to talk about ventilation once again. It's extremely important that the attic is able to "breathe"; that is, air has to be able to move into and out of the attic in both summer and winter. Air should be able to come in through vents in the soffit at the bottom of the roof and out through vents at the peak of the roof. This air flow is critical for removing heat and moisture from the attic. So you'll want to be sure the insulation that's put in the attic doesn't choke off this air flow. A conscientious builder will install polystyrene spacers in the insulation to ensure an unobstructed air passageway from the overhang at the soffit to the roof peak.

Ceiling insulation

As we've said, ceiling insulation will happen later in the construction process since, well, there are no ceilings yet. But since we're talking about insulation, we're going to discuss it now.

On flat ceilings, your builder will typically use the loose-blown fiberglass insulation. When applied to a depth of 15 inches, this insulation will provide an insulation value of R-38.

In sloped or vaulted ceilings, blown insulation has a tendency to shift and slide; therefore; your builder should use the standard batt insulation, which can be secured in place.

Floor insulation

Homes built correctly on a slab foundation are already insulated below the floors around the perimeter with insulation board and don't require any additional insulation. However, with a crawlspace foundation, the block or poured walls around the perimeter of the foundation need to be insulated. This is done in one of two ways. One way is to hang batts against the interior walls of the crawlspace. The other is to blow in an insulation mixed with a resin that adheres to the walls of the crawlspace.

With the insulation, plumbing, HVAC, and electrical systems in place, your new home is coming to life. But, it's the next stage of the construction process—the interior completion—when you will see your home start to look like a real home on the inside. There's still a lot to do. But with each completed step in the next process, you'll see your dream come closer and closer to reality.

☕ Coffee Break: Step back and consider the big picture.

Now that all the necessary mechanical system infrastructures are in place and approved by the city (and your builder), you have another incredible photo opportunity. So step back and grab your camera. This point in the construction process is your last chance to record the exact locations of the mechanical systems networks within the framework of your home.

And why should this be of photographic interest to you? It's ugly...

Accurate visual records showing the placement of pipes and wires will prove valuable when you want to hang that mahogany-framed, velvet painting of Elvis on the foyer wall. You can reduce the risk of putting a nail through a water pipe or shorting out your electrical system if you know where these things are before you start using your hammer. Additionally, any future plans for remodeling your home may be significantly influenced by the known locations of the mechanical systems. And should you ever sell your home, having these visual records is a nice resale bonus for the prospective buyer.

So start snapping pictures now. Your builder can help identify rooms and areas of the home that you're photographing, as well as describe the systems to you and how they affect the different parts of your home. Be sure to accurately label all photographs!

CHAPTER EIGHT

Your new home gets all dressed up on the inside.

Once the mechanical systems are in place and the walls and floors have been thoroughly insulated, the home can proceed to the interior finish stage of construction. The *interior finish stage* is the "makeover" stage of the home. Wall surfaces and trim are put up and painted or stained. Floors are covered with carpet, laminate, tile, vinyl, or other materials. Lighting and plumbing fixtures and select appliances are installed at this time. In short, all the finishing touches that complete your home's interior are going in now.

Keep in mind that each activity at this stage has been scheduled and is done in a sequence that your builder has predetermined to be the most efficient. Also, many things are happening simultaneously now, keeping the construction process moving smoothly.

☑ FIREPLACE INSTALLATION

Keeping The Home Fires Burning

One of the first elements installed in the interior finish stage is the fireplace. As with other larger fixtures, such as your bathtub and shower, the fireplace is usually installed before the

IN THIS CHAPTER

WE'LL COVER:

- ☐ **Fireplace installation**
- ☐ **Drywall**
  Drywall stocking
  Drywall installation
  Interior wall prime
- ☐ **Interior trim**
- ☐ **Drywall repairs**
- ☐ **Interior painting**
- ☐ **Cabinets counter tops and vanities**
- ☐ **HVAC, plumbing and electrical finish**
- ☐ **Floor coverings**
  Vinyl
  Laminate
  Ceramic
  Carpet
  Trim finish
- ☐ **Accessories**

| Start | Month 2 | Month 3 | Month 4 | Month 5 | Finish |

Many prefabricated fireplaces have a 'cold air feed' that brings air in from outside the house to feed the fire instead of pulling air from inside the home.

Today's manufactured fireplaces are safe, cost effective, and easy to install. The fireplace is placed during the mechanical installation phase of construction before the drywall is installed.

drywall work begins. Once the fireplace unit and flue are installed, drywall will cover the unfinished portions of these units, hiding them from view.

Sometimes, fireplaces are constructed with masonry products onsite. But most fireplaces today arrive as prefabricated firebox units. These units provide a better value for the dollar than traditional masonry fireplaces. They use an outside combustion source that draws air from outside the home to feed the fire, reducing the draw on the home's heated interior air, resulting in energy cost savings.

This type of fireplace is also built with a double- or triple-wall chimney system. The outer layer of this system is made with galvanized steel, and the inner layer is stainless steel. Between the two layers is an airspace that effectively protects the chimney chase from excess heat by insulating the inner flue, which contains hot air and gases. Also, your builder is required by code to install a fire-stop material where the fireplace and the chimney penetrate the framing.

The flue runs up the chimney chase and outside the home. At the top of the chimney where the smoke and gases are expelled, your builder is required to install a termination cap, which serves multiple purposes. First, the termination cap prevents large sparks and ashes from escaping and presenting a fire hazard to your roof (or your neighbor's roof). It also reduces heavy air drafts from blowing down the flue. And it stops small birds and animals, as well as rain and snow, from entering your home. As with most products, you can buy a nice chimney cap that fits snugly and unobtrusively...or you can buy a cheap aluminum cap that looks sort of like a mushroom. A conscientious builder will also make sure the area behind the fireplace is well insulated; it's one of those areas where drafts are common.

The first step in the drywall process is to deliver the correct quantities of materials to the home. It is more efficient to mechanically stock this heavy drywall into the appropriate rooms than to...

☑ DRYWALL

Wall Together Now

Finally, it's time to put up the walls inside your home. And these days, that means drywall.

Drywall is essentially a board, usually composed of gypsum with a paper facing and backing, that comes in panels that are four feet wide and either eight or 16 feet long. These panels are attached to the interior framework of the house to form the ceilings and then the walls. The drywall process is composed of three primary activities: stocking, installation, and repair. The first two of these activities can take anywhere from five to 15 days, depending on the size of your home and the skill of the drywall crew. We're going to look at stocking and installation now.

Drywall stocking

The first step in the drywall process is the delivery of drywall to your homesite and allocating it to the appropriate areas throughout the home. Simple, right?

Not really. Because of the massive size and weight of some drywall boards, the drywall installers often use a special hoist to feed stacks of drywall through open windows or doors throughout the home. In some cases, getting drywall to the second floor may require cutting out a piece of the sheathing—but it's easily repaired. It's a comparatively cumbersome process—but one that will save time in the long run.

...carry it up the stairs by hand.

Start		Month 2	Month 3	Month 4	Month 5	Finish

Your new home gets all dressed up inside.

In the bathrooms, around tubs and showers where excessive moisture is present, your builder should take extra precautions to protect the drywall from water damage. Conscientious builders will use special drywall boards known as greenboard that are treated with a wax-based, water-resistant green coating. Your builder may also choose to use an even more durable, waterproof masonry board in the areas that will come into direct contact with water. Your builder may also use a variety of different drywalls in different areas of the home to comply with local codes.

The drywall installers start by hanging the drywall on the ceilings.

Two other types of drywall are used in conjunction with white gypsum board. Water-resistant green board, and semi-waterproof masonry board are used in the home's "wetter" areas.

Drywall installation

Installation is, itself, a multi-step process that includes hanging, taping, finishing, and texturing. In the hanging stage, 1/2-inch thick drywall is nailed to studs to form the interior walls. Ceilings and walls adjacent to the exterior or non-living areas are hung with a slightly thicker, 5/8-inch drywall, which should be secured with both nails and screws. The screws provide additional strength and help reduce nail "pops" that occur when the nail head breaks through the wall's finished surface after the drywall and finish coat have dried.

After the drywall has been hung, first on the ceilings, then on the walls, a different team of specialists comes in for the finish work. The drywall finish crew will complete all the necessary steps to prepare the wall surfaces to receive their covering of paint or wallpaper. The crew will:

- Cover corners with a fitted metal strip, referred to as a corner bead. Exposed corners of the drywall are particularly vulnerable to damage. The corner bead provides strength and durability at these critical areas.
- Cover these metal strips with joint compound so that they are indistinguishable from the other drywall surfaces.
- Apply joint compound (or "mud," as it's known in the trade) over any joint or seam and nail/screw hole in the drywall.
- Apply a heavy paper tape strip over the seams.
- Apply two final coats of joint compound across the joints and seams after the initial layer of compound dries.
- Texture or treat the ceilings with joint compound to create subtle patterns for decorative effect.

The drywall finish is critical to the overall aesthetics of the home, so the builder needs to carefully monitor each step of the process. Once the drywall process has been completed, the walls are ready to be primed for painting.

Interior wall prime

At this point, the walls we just installed have a relatively rough and porous drywall surface and tend to soak in a lot of paint on the first coat. For this reason, interior wall painting is a two-step process. Your builder starts with an initial or "primer" coat of paint. The primer coat fills the pores in the walls and woodwork, making the final coat more effective in covering the wall surface. Note that primer isn't necessarily a special paint. It may simply be the first coat of a good-quality interior wall paint.

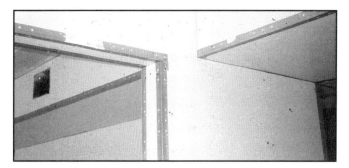

After all the surfaces are covered with drywall, the installers join the corner seams with metal corner bead. This corner bead ties the two drywall planes together and reinforces the corner.

After the drywall hanging crew completes the installation the finishing crew begins to mud and tape the seams and mud the nail or screw holes.

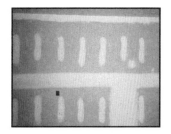

Seams and hole patches are sanded and the process repeated until a smooth surface is ready for the primer coat of paint.

L On The Level:

At this point, the overhead garage door will be installed. And, believe it or not, your garage will actually start being used! It'll serve as the central receiving hub for most material deliveries made to the homesite. This way, items can be temporarily stored and protected from the elements before they're installed.

The trim carpenter also installs baseboards, window trim, mantles, and wood caps on half walls.

Fireplace mantels can be a kit purchase, or, in this case, custom built to serve as the focal point of the room.

The interior trim carpenter's work is often the focal point for each room. Here the beautiful spindle and hand rail vertically defines the entry space.

The interior trim carpenter starts by setting the wall and base cabinets in the kitchens, baths, and perhaps the family room.

☑ INTERIOR TRIM

Trimming Up The Walls

The *interior trim process* is the delivery and installation of all ornamental and decorative wood pieces. Trimwork is used to facilitate transitions from one material to another; to conceal any unfinished areas or unsightly joints; and to add depth and design to the home. The trim package includes baseboards, door and window casings, moldings, hand-crafted mantels, attic access stairs, stair rails and spindles, shelves, and all interior doors.

If you're planning to stain the trimwork in your new home, it's important for your builder to use a wood that has an appealing natural grain. Most builders will use solid white pine, poplar, cherry, oak, or other hardwoods for stained trim work; the specific type used generally depends on availability, cost, and your own preference. In cases where the trim will be painted (which is much more common today than stained trim), the grain of the wood is not as important, and builders commonly use trim pieces that are manufactured using a combination of woods. (See Table 7.1 to consider the pros and cons of painting and staining.)

Since the main purpose of trim is cosmetic, it's important to have professionals—trim carpenters—who have an eye for beauty and detail working on this part of your home. As an example, it's standard for interior trim carpenters to make sure all nail heads are below the surface of the wood to ensure a smooth, clean finish. These holes are filled with a wood putty compound before painting or staining.

Perhaps the best example of the meticulous care and craftsmanship required of trim carpenters is (or should be) your home's staircase. The stairway rail, spindles, and moldings often require hundreds of difficult, angled or mitered cuts to fit together properly.

The trim takes about two or three days to install. Everything except the quarter-round trim that's used to cover the edges where the floor covering meets the baseboard is installed now. The quarter-round, as you might guess, has to be installed after the flooring.

The interior trim carpenter also installs the garage pegboard. Pegboard helps the homeowner keep the garage organized, leaving room for the cars in the garage. Organized garages have a ripple effect. The neater the garage, the more likely the car will be kept inside the garage, thus keeping the streetscape 'cleaner.'

DRYWALL REPAIRS

The Final Fixes

At this point in the construction process, most of the necessary components of the walls, ceilings, and trim are in place. Your new home is ready to begin receiving its final wall covering. Right?

Nope. It's time for one last—and necessary—bit of repair.

After the interior trim work has been completed and the walls have been primed to receive paint, the wall surfaces are given a quality control check. The builder looks for flaws caused by damage, unsatisfactory workmanship, or natural settling. Regardless of how skilled the drywall workers are, some maintenance will be required. It's typical and natural for small cracks to form, nail "pops" to occur, or the corner bead to need another layer of "mud." This is why your builder will pre-schedule a time for drywall repairs.

The drywall contractor often uses a light to magnify imperfections during the drywall touchup step. This process far exceeds the industry drywall finish specifications.

Porter Paints • www.porterpaints.com

For more than 80 years, Porter has been making the superior interior paints that builders and homeowners prefer. Better formulations and ingredients mean Porter paint lasts longer than many other brands. There are fewer solvents, less water, and more hiding pigments in Porter paints, so they go on smoother, spread farther, and cover more wall than lesser paints; you might say there's more "paint" in Porter paints! Although they may be a bit more expensive up front, over the long-term, Porter paints cost less per square foot to use than lesser-quality brands, making Porter an all-around better value.

 INTERIOR PAINTING

Another Coat For The Walls

Now that your builder has touched up the walls and prepared them for painting, we're ready to apply the beautiful paint colors you selected a few months ago.

Well, we're almost ready. Actually, the trim has to be primed, sanded, and given a final coat first. These days, most of the interior wood for your home comes pre-primed. If the trim work on the home is going to be stained instead of painted, the stain application is performed at this time, as well—although, in some cases, the trim is stained prior to installation, because it's easier to get smooth, even stain coverage before the trim is attached to the wall.

After the primer coat on the walls dries, the painters lightly sand the entire wall to ensure a smooth, blemish-free surface for the paint. Then the final coat of paint is applied to the walls.

A final paint touchup takes place immediately before closing, after all other activities have been completed and the chance for a nick or mar in the paint job is minimal. Your builder may leave unused paint and exact color formulas with you after closing so you can touch up paint yourself when you need to. And you'll need to. In general, you'll want to repaint every three to five years to keep your home looking fresh and clean, and as often as every six months in especially high-traffic areas frequented by children.

Builders generally use flat, water-based latex paints on interior wall surfaces and semi-gloss

The finish coat of paint is usually a flat latex paint rolled on the walls and...

	Pros	Cons
Paint	• Less expensive than stain due to less labor and a less expensive grade of wood • Easier to touch up • Covers completely and uniformly • Easier to match colors throughout home	• Seams have a tendency to show • Higher maintenance (shows dirt, scuffs)
Stain	• Seams blend with wood grain • Shows beauty of wood grain • Lower maintenance (hides dirt and scuffs better) • Higher perceived value	• Harder to match colors of wood • Can show imperfections of wood • More expensive due to need for higher grade of wood and higher labor costs to achieve the desired look • More difficult to touch up

latex on trim work. Flat paints dry to a low-luster finish, while semi-gloss paints have a high-luster satin finish. Although there are "scrubbable" paints available, they're not generally used by new homebuilders because they're more expensive, and their glossier finish is less attractive on most of the walls in your home. (Don't scrub flat paint, by the way. Scrubbing the walls will usually result in scrubbing off the paint right along with the fingerprints.) Eggshell finish paints—with a level of gloss somewhere between flat and semi-gloss—are more moisture resistant and are often used on bathroom walls. You'll just want to keep in mind that any glossier paint will have a tendency to "flash"; that is, spots you touch up will appear to be shinier than the rest of the wall.

You may also be wondering why your builder doesn't paint the ceilings in your home. Simply put, they don't have to be painted. The material used for your ceilings already has white paint in it. Essentially, your ceilings are painted before they're installed!

...enamel paint brushed on the woodwork.

Aristokraft Cabinets • www.aristokraft.com

Cabinets need to be special: not only beautiful, but durable and functional, as well. Aristokraft makes superior cabinets that offer all three, in an abundance of styles and finishes to match your taste. Plus, Aristokraft is the only cabinet manufacturer to carry the Good Housekeeping Seal—your assurance of quality and performance.

Aristokraft is part of MasterBrand Cabinets, a Jasper, Indiana-based company whose other brands include Decora, Diamond, Kemper, NHB, and Schrock. The people at MasterBrand focus on listening to today's families, then creating the products that meet their needs. MasterBrand is committed to providing superior cabinets at fair prices, honoring every promise, and helping families turn their dreams into reality.

CABINETS, COUNTERTOPS, AND VANITIES

Nooks, Crannies, And Open Spaces

You need places to put things away and places to lay them out when you need to use them in the kitchen, bath, and other areas of your home where storage is required.

Cabinets

Although you may require cabinets in many rooms in your home, you'll almost always have them in the kitchen and bathrooms. Because of the craftsmanship involved in making cabinets, they must be ordered from a cabinetmaker far in advance of installation to ensure timely delivery. For this reason, builders generally can't make changes to your original cabinet selection once the construction process has begun...so choose carefully now! You have a wide variety of cabinet styles to consider, so keep in mind such factors as wood content, assembly technique, finish, hardware, and the manufacturer's warranty. Generally speaking, the higher the wood content, the more expensive the cabinet.

Typically, the cabinets, countertops, and vanities are delivered with the trim package and are stored in your home's garage until installation. The cabinets come in sections that are set in position according to the floor plan and attached to the floor, walls, and adjoining sections using clamps and wood screws.

Thinking about custom-built cabinets? You should know that even minimal custom cabinetry and built-ins can be as expensive as an entire manufactured kitchen cabinet package. Do it if you must...but consider your options carefully.

Countertops

Once the cabinet sections are in place, the carpenters will install the countertops. Countertops are most commonly made of a smooth, durable laminate veneer surface. Other countertop options include ceramic tile and solid surface materials such as marble, granite, and specially manufactured surfaces.

Each surface has its pros and cons. Laminates come in an incredible range of styles and colors and are reasonably priced. But they're easier to scratch and more difficult to repair. They also don't resist heat as well, so you don't want to set a hot saucepan on laminate. And lots of people don't like the looks of visible seams—or the possibility of water damage at those seams—inherent in installed laminate countertops. Solid surfaces, on the other hand, are strong and durable and resist scratches and burns. If you do hurt them, the marks can generally be erased with light sanding. But solid surfaces are expensive. Color choices are limited. And installation of solid surface tops may require some special provisions. Ceramic tile gives you more durability and more choices. But it's also expensive to install, and the grout can be challenging to clean. Nothing's perfect; weigh the advantages and disadvantages and make the choice that best suites your lifestyle. Laminate tops still seem to rule the roost when all the cost/benefit analysis is done.

Cabinets are key to an attractive and functional kitchen. Aristokraft cabinets offers several lines of styles, colors, and finishes. (See Product Spotlight)

✖ Hard Hat Area: Watch for falling building standards.

It's not that difficult to get cabinets that look nice on the outside. That's why it's all the most important to pay attention to detail when choosing cabinets for your new home. Things to look for:

- Drawers. Do you have enough of them? Drawers are relatively expensive, so it's a place some builders will try to skimp. Many times, new homeowners discover too late that their second bath room has no drawers for kids' toothbrushes and toiletries.
- Dovetailing. One sure sign of a well-constructed drawer is dovetail jointed corners. Cheaply made drawers are stapled at the corners.
- Undermounted hardware. For your drawers, undermounted slides are much more durable and dependable than sidemounted hardware.
- Shelving. Some cabinets have thin shelves that will bow under the weight of plates and bowls. Don't fall for a pretty face. Take a closer look at your cabinets. Truly, it's what's inside that counts.

| Start | | Month 2 | Month 3 | Month 4 | Month 5 | Finish |

Your new home gets all dressed up inside.

Vanity tops

Time to install the vanity tops in your bathrooms. Most vanity tops today are made of high-quality, reinforced fiberglass in cultured marble simulation. Fiberglass molded vanities are generally preferred because they can be molded to any shape and texture, enabling the sink bowl and vanity to be one continuous, molded piece. Unlike ceramic tops, fiberglass vanities and sinks also offer the advantage of having a strong resistance to chipping and cracking.

The finishing touches include installing sinks, faucets...

☑ HVAC, PLUMBING, AND ELECTRICAL FINISH
Systematically Finishing Your Systems

As part of the final interior finish, your builder will schedule the plumbers, the electricians, and the heating and cooling subcontractors to come back to perform their final duties. In this stage of the construction process, all the cosmetic details such as outlet covers, vent grills, and lights are set in place. Then the utilities are connected and you can actually plug things in and turn on the water and condition the air throughout your new home.

HVAC finish steps

The HVAC finish begins with the actual installation of the heat pump, or furnace and air conditioner. Once the units are installed, all the necessary connections are made and the system is charged with refrigerant, the heating and cooling agent that enables a heat pump and air conditioner to operate. When the equipment is in place and connected, the system is activated and tested for at least 24 hours to ensure that it functions properly. Also, all the final details related to the HVAC system are handled at this time; for example, a 1/2-inch PVC drain line that runs from the air handler to a floor drain to catch condensation is installed, as are all the registers and grills over vents and air returns. Finally, the system is "balanced" so that the right amount of air is being delivered to each room of the home. This balance may also need to be adjusted after you furnish the home.

Kohler Fixtures · www.kohler.com

Kohler has long been recognized as the industry leader in innovation and design of kitchen and bath fixtures. Yet, Kohler started out in quite a different business. The company was founded in Sheboygan, Wisconsin, in 1873. John Michael Kohler started a modest foundry and machine shop that produced cast iron plowshares and other agricultural equipment for area farmers, as well as decorative furniture, hitching posts, and ornamental iron castings. Then in 1883, Kohler took a product in his line, heated it to 1700° F and sprinkled it with enamel powder. Placing a picture of it in his catalog, he called it "a horse trough/hog scalder... when furnished with four legs will serve as a bathtub." The innovative idea marked the company's initial introduction into the plumbing business.

Today, Kohler is still an innovator and a leader. From the most enduring traditional designs to the boldest, most forward-looking styles, Kohler is the name people around the world associate with the very best in kitchen and bath fashions.

THE BOLD LOOK OF **KOHLER**.®

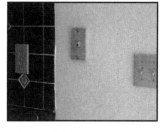

...electrical plates...

...lighting....

...and closet shelving.

Plumbing finish steps

Step one in finishing the plumbing is installing the water heater. The plumber connects the water heater to the 1/2-inch copper supply and distribution lines with a non-lead solder. Builders typically install a 40-gallon, quick-recovery electric water heater, which is generally more than sufficient to support the water use of a four-member family. But you need to consider your own water use. Do you take lots of baths in an oversized whirlpool tub? You may need a bigger water heater to handle the volume.

Next, the kitchen sink is set in place and two-inch PVC drain lines are connected. The dishwasher is then set in place, and one 3/8-inch copper line is spliced from the kitchen sink supply line and connected to the dishwasher. Then the one-inch plastic drain tube from the dishwasher is connected to the garbage disposal.

Toilets? Check. They are supplied and installed by the plumber next. Toilets require a wax "O-ring" to be positioned where the drain connects. This wax ring serves as an oversized gasket, sealing the drain connection. Once in place, the water supply line is connected to the bottom of the toilet reservoir tank.

Next, plumbers attach hose spigots, or silcocks, to the exterior of the home. Your builder should use only high-quality silcocks that are freeze-proof and have a vacuum breaker. These features will reduce the likelihood of water freezing inside the valve during the winter, which could cause the pipes to rupture. These nifty valves work only if the water can drain from the silcock, so remember to disconnect your hoses *before* the first freezing night of the season.

The locations of the silcocks can vary by design, but generally your builder will position the silcocks conveniently and logically near the places you're most likely to need them. Usually, one is positioned on the exterior wall adjacent to the kitchen sink. A tap is made from the cold water line under the sink and runs through the wall to the exterior of the home to supply water to this silcock. Another is placed in the front of the home and will have its own supply line rough-in.

Finally, the plumbers will install and connect all the necessary plumbing fixtures to the sinks, tubs, and showers. A conscientious builder will put a grade of fixtures in the home that is consistent with its aesthetic style, falls within your budget parameters, and has a well-earned reputation for quality and durability. Kohler for example, is a respected manufacturere that makes a broad range of fixtures for many budgets aand decorating styles (see *Product Spotlight*).

When the plumbing finish is complete, the plumbers will turn on the main water valve, usually located in the utility closet, and check all plumbing systems for leaks or other problems. You've got water!

Electrical finish steps

Now how about getting some power? After turning off the main breaker located in the circuit breaker box, the electrician will connect all electrical receptacles, switches, telephone jacks, and cable outlets in your home. Next, the electrician will complete any necessary connections to appliances or utilities such as the dishwasher, range hood, microwave, water heater, and heat pump. The electric range does not need to be independently wired, because it usually comes with a pre-wired plug.

When the wiring is complete, the electricians turn the main breaker back on and test all the receptacles, switches, and appliances. If all are working properly, the cover plates are mounted over the outlets and switches, and circuit breakers are labeled at the control panel.

During the electrical finish, your builder will also arrange for a lighting specialist to come in and install all remaining exterior and interior lighting fixtures. They typically install light bulbs as well, to make sure the fixtures are working properly.

☑ FLOOR COVERINGS

Getting Down With Your Floor Covering

The floor covering installation is performed near the end of the construction process in order to preserve its cleanliness and minimize damage. In our experience, floor coverings can be a source of high emotion and deep distress for some new homeowners; since some construction activity remains, it's still relatively easy for damage to occur, and homeowners often want an entire flooring area replaced if there's a little nick or scratch. Actually, most damage can be repaired if it's caught early (and, in truth, flooring often comes out of the box with slight imperfections that require touchup). Emotions aside, fixing a chip or small scratch is a reasonable request. If your new car had a small scratch in a door, you wouldn't expect the

Vinyl "sheet-goods" are more resistant to moisture and therefore are often put in wetter areas such as baths and laundry rooms. Here the installer trims the roll of vinyl to the base of the vanity cabinets.

dealer to replace the entire car or even the door, would you? If you've chosen the right builder, you can be sure that great care will be taken to protect your floor coverings throughout the rest of the construction process and that any repairs will be done in a professional manner.

Now that the home is ready to receive its final floor coverings, the experienced builder will conduct a final inspection of the drywall, trim, and cabinets and make any necessary repairs before flooring installation actually begins. This inspection also includes rechecking the subfloor for squeaks or unevenness.

Now let's take a quick look at the types of floor covering materials that might be used in your new home, including vinyl, laminate, ceramic tile, and carpet.

Vinyl

Vinyl is one of the most versatile and durable flooring materials available. It comes in innumerable styles, colors and designs, giving you more options than you may actually want for your flooring selections. Vinyl has the distinct advantage of usually being the most cost-efficient floor covering material, as well. For these reasons, vinyl has become a very popular choice of homeowners for high-traffic areas such as the kitchen, entryway, utility room, and bathrooms.

Vinyl generally comes in three basic forms: sheets, tiles, and planks. You and your builder can choose the type of vinyl you want, based on your budget and the look you are trying to achieve.

| Start | | Month 2 | Month 3 | Month 4 | Month 5 | Finish |

Laminate

Laminate flooring is a relatively new innovation—but one that has quickly taken the new home construction industry by storm. These new laminate floors are extremely durable compared with other hard-surface floors, such as wood and ceramic. They're more moisture resistant and much less expensive, too. And they're visually stunning: technology has advanced to the point where the laminate floors are nearly identical in appearance to the wood and stone and ceramic floors they mimic.

While laminates are great alternatives, they're a little more expensive than vinyl. And they're not bulletproof. These floors should be protected—especially at seams. (By the way: all floors have seams that are visible and change with weather, usage, and aging.)

One of today's most popular flooring choices is laminate floors. Mannington makes many great patterns that (very realistically) appear to be wood or ceramic tile. (See Product Spotlight)

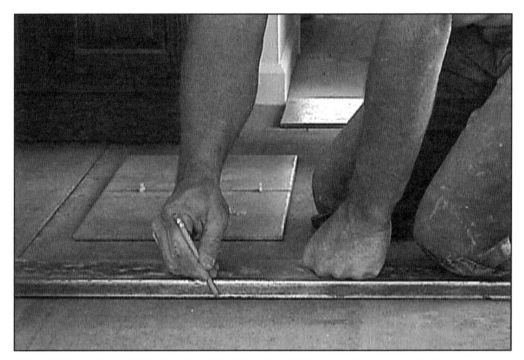

1. Ceramic tile requires a reinforced, stable, and level floor. Ceramic tile is a multi-step process. First the floor centerline is marked and the tiles laid out.

2. The floor is then prepared with a tile adhesive compound. The tiles are set in place and allowed 24 hours to set.

3. Then spaces between the tiles are then grouted. This grout should be treated with a sealant 60 to 90 days after home ownership. The entire ceramic tile process can take 2-4 days.

4. After the hard flooring surfaces are installed, it is wise to cover the flooring with protective paper.

Ceramic tile

Ceramic tile installation may apply not only to the flooring, but to several different areas of the home, including shower and tub surrounds, fireplace surrounds, and kitchen countertops. Ceramic tile is glued to the surface and allowed to cure for about 24 hours. Then the installers come back to uniformly fill the gaps between the tiles with grout. Grout helps prevent water from penetrating the tile surface and damaging the area below. We strongly suggest that you let the grout cure for a few months, then apply a protective grout sealer to further help protect the integrity of the tiled area.

Ceramic tile installation, depending on the area, may take a little longer than vinyl or laminate installation due to the curing process and additional precision needed to assure the grout lines are uniform. Also, a ceramic tile floor may require a more heavily reinforced flooring system; since ceramic is so much heavier than other floor coverings, it may move and crack unless the support system is sturdier. This is one reason why the decision to go with a ceramic tile floor should be made before the home is framed.

Wood

Hardwood floors—and certain softer woods, such as pine—are gorgeous and desirable. You'll get no quibbles from us about this. They add warmth and traditional beauty to virtually any room in your home. And most reputable builders will install hardwood floors if you prefer them. Just know that they're relatively difficult to maintain, especially if you have kids or pets who are going to scratch the heck out of them. And hardwoods are expensive—maybe even thousands of dollars more per room than other flooring options.

The carpet installers start the carpet process by nailing tack strips around the perimeter of the rooms to be carpeted.

The carpet pad is laid up to the tack strips. Pads vary in thickness and density. Sometimes the home-owner can feel density difference under the carpet. This is normal.

Carpet

Only after all other interior finish work is completed will the wall-to-wall carpet be installed. Why? One word: cleanliness. Paint or stain drops, grease, and muddy boots can "leave their mark" on freshly installed carpet. But don't worry: today's carpet is extremely resilient, and there are lots of commercially available carpet cleaners that will easily remove most stains.

Shaw Industries Carpet • www.shawinc.com

Shaw Industries, a subsidiary of Berkshire Hathaway, Inc., is the world's largest manufacturer of carpet and other floor coverings, including rugs, ceramic, hardwood, and laminate flooring for residential and commercial applications throughout the world; in fact, Shaw manufactures more than 600 million square yards of floor covering every year—enough to wrap a six-foot wide path around the earth's equator seven times.

Headquartered in Dalton, Georgia, Shaw got its start in 1946 as Star Dye Company, a small business that dyed tufted scatter rugs. The company's 30,000-plus employees perform roles that encompass every aspect of production, from fiber extrusion to state-of-the-art tufting, research and development to final delivery. With more than 25,000 styles and colors, Shaw makes floor coverings to meet the unique styles of consumers everywhere no matter what their style.

Carpet generally comes in 12-foot widths, so seaming pieces together happens in every home. Seams can be virtually invisible except on carpets with lots of texture, like berbers and freizes.

It usually takes one or two days to lay carpet, depending on the amount of carpet and the difficulty of the installation. To begin, the floors are carefully cleaned and cleared of debris. Tack strips are then placed around the perimeter of the installation area. These tack strips, as their name suggests, are narrow strips of wood spiked with rows of small, pro-truding tacks that are used to secure the carpet edges to the perimeter of the room.

Next, carpet padding is cut to fit the area and stapled to the underlying floor surface. Padding provides additional cushioning to the carpet and also helps the carpet wear in more controlled patterns. This padding is often made from recycled materials that can sometimes be felt as slight varia-tions in texture as you walk across the carpet. So please keep this in mind before you call your builder to insist that some-one has left a hammer under your carpet. (Trust us, it almost never happens.)

The seamed carpet is then stretched over the perimeter tack strips. Dragging furniture across the carpet can loosen or stretch the carpet, requiring the homeowner to have the carpet re-stretched.

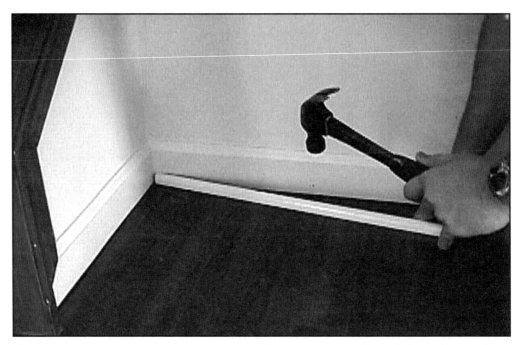

The interior trim carpenter returns to the home for trim finish where quarter round is installed around hard surfaces and any trim adjustments are made.

Generally speaking you get what you pay for in carpet. High quality manufacturers-like Shaw Industries Carpet have several quality lines of carpet in varying weights, styles and colors (see *Product Spotlight*).

Finally, the carpet is cut and positioned over the padding. Any seams in the carpet are joined with a heat-activated tape applied to the underside of the carpet. Then the carpet is stretched over the tack strips and tucked under the baseboard trim. In areas where carpet meets vinyl, laminate, tile, or hardwood, the edges of the carpet are either finished with a brass carpet strip or curled under and secured in place. Some carpet styles, such as berber, show seams more readily than other styles. This is because berber is a "loop pile" product, as opposed to "cut pile" products whose seams are easier to hide.

Flooring trim finish

Now that all the floor coverings are installed, the trim carpenters can return briefly (and, hopefully, with clean boots) to install the final trim pieces. The final trim finish consists of installing quarter round molding. Quarter round is the small, rounded trim piece at the base of the walls used to hide the transition from baseboard to flooring. The trim finishers may also make any last-minute corrections to doors that may be hindered from swinging open by the carpet, or to any other small trim pieces that need attention.

ACCESSORIES

Accessories, Accessories, Accessories

And more accessories—and installing them is the next step. These accessories include the bathroom mirrors, shower doors, towel racks, toilet tissue holders, doorknobs, doorstops, dead-bolts, kick plates, and other hardware. Closet shelves, hanger rods, and organizers are also installed at this time.

Think you'd like to save a little money and do all this stuff yourself? Don't do it. With everything you'll have to do between closing and moving into your home, you'll appreciate all this stuff being done for you. And frankly, a new home should have all of these things included and finished before you walk into it for the first time. You'll have enough to do moving, organizing, decorating, and arranging your home to keep you busy for several months—trust us on this one. Besides, another great benefit of a new home is the warranty that comes with it. You could void parts of the warranty by doing the work yourself.

Okay. So we've put the house up and covered it. We've added the mechanical systems and completed the finish work on those systems and the appliances they support. We've put up the walls after insulation and painted them. Doors and windows are in. The floors are covered and the plumbing and lighting fixtures are installed and ready to use.

While your home is nearing completion, you'll notice that "bringing in the furniture" is not the next step. Bear with us. We're almost home.

Near the end of the construction phase, the construction locks are changed out to permanent locks to protect the nearly finished home.

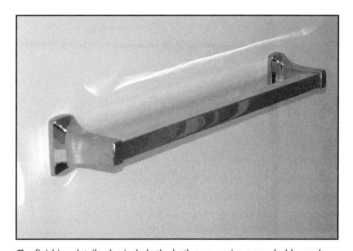

The finishing details also include the bath accessories, paper holder, and door stops.

CHAPTER NINE

We add all the little things that make the big things look even better...and hand your new home over to you.

As your home nears completion, you're no doubt starting to get even more excited. You're anxious about your move-in date. Your builder has now brought the process full circle: from a vision to a floor plan; from a floor plan to a skeleton; from a skeleton to a structure with a complex system of modern conveniences; and from a complex structure to a home—your home, which is actually the beginning of another vision.

However, there are still a few more details that have to be attended to before your builder can present you with the keys to the vision. Your builder still has to complete a few things before closing: landscaping, final installation of appliances, miscellaneous repairs and touchups, a final cleaning, and preparation of the legal documents required for closing. So, if you're ready, let's start getting finished.

✔ EXTERIOR ELEMENTS

Once Around The Outside

Now that all the heavy equipment is on its way out, your builder can concentrate on all the things that are going to beautify and complete the exterior of your home—starting with the concrete work.

IN THIS CHAPTER WE'LL COVER:

☐ **Exterior elements**
- Exterior concrete finish
- Mailbox
- Window and door screens
- Decks and patios
- Landscaping

☐ **Final interior improvements**
- Final appliance installation
- Quality review and punch list completion
- Final cleaning

☐ **Home presentation and closing**
- Final inspection
- Closing package

It's important that you know what you're getting with your poured concrete patio. If you have any future aspirations of building a screened porch or three-seasons room on the concrete, then you'd better make sure your patio has footings and is structurally ready for that addition. This decision must be made at the foundation stage for economy's sake. Most good builders will make patio footings an option...and any builder worth his or her salt will certainly build the screened porch for you if you select it before home construction starts.

Driveways, sidewalks, and patios may all be poured with different strength concrete, depending on the climate and specifications.

Exterior concrete finish

Sometimes concrete work on driveways and sidewalks is completed in the foundation and framing stage. However, a professional builder may delay pouring some driveways or walks until after heavy construction is complete to ensure that they are not damaged. Your builder may also choose to wait and pour several sections at once for the sake of efficiency and consistency. Either way, these items must be complete before the home can be considered ready for closing.

You may notice that the color of the concrete poured at this time doesn't exactly match the color of the concrete poured earlier. There's simply no avoiding this situation. Concrete mixed and poured in separate batches—even on the same day—will vary a bit in color.

Your mailbox

In communities where many homes are under construction, the builder may prefer to delay mailbox installation until immediately before completion to protect it from dirt and damage during the construction process.

Many times, a community or neighborhood association requires uniformity in the style and color of the mailbox and its post. In these cases, you don't get to select your own mailbox. A mailbox installer will usually schedule groups of mailbox installations on the same day for the sake of efficiency, which may dictate the exact date of installation. Sometimes your local post office will supply the community with temporary boxes in a central location away from construction until the permanent boxes can be installed.

Window and door screens

Most builders will provide new fiberglass mesh screens for all windows and patio doors in your new home. Fiberglass mesh screens are typically of higher quality and lower cost—and are easier to clean—than the older metal wire mesh screens. Because they're susceptible to damage and tearing, window and door screens are scheduled for installation very late in the construction process.

The mailbox is installed near the end of the construction process. Sometimes a builder may choose to put in a temporary mailbox until the lawn can be installed if winter weather delays the sod and seed.

💱 Our Two Cents:

Seal your concrete.

Huh? Isn't concrete pretty tough stuff?

Well, yes. But if you don't apply a sealant, you're going to have problems down the road. Your drive and garage are going to be damaged by salt: Driveway Enemy #1 and the primary source of concrete deterioration.

But, you say, you never use salt on your driveway. Doesn't matter. Your city or town uses plenty on your local roadways to melt ice and snow. Your car picks up salt as you drive along. When you park in your garage or on your driveway, the salt falls off with the melting snow and can pit the concrete.

So how do you protect yourself? Seal your concrete. It's a simple task that takes not much more than a garden sprayer and a sealant that's available at your local hardware store. And it's up to you—not your builder—to seal it and maintain it.

Seal your concrete. 'Nuff said.

Screens are also installed late in the construction process to keep them clean and minimize damage to the screen material.

We add all the little things that make the big things look even better...

You may have noticed that part of the first step in building any new home community is to virtually strip the entire site of topsoil. This is a necessary step. The developer has to strip the site to properly grade the land and prepare it for building. So how come your builder doesn't put the topsoil back when the homes are built?

The real answer is, it's neither practical nor necessary. You may think you need that topsoil to grow your lawn, but you don't. Great stands of grass can be grown with a good fertilization and lawn care program regardless of soil conditions.

Decks and other outdoor landscape treatments are done late in the construction process after all the heavy equipment has left the site.

Decks and patios

Decks and patios are important features for many homeowners because they create additional "living space" outside the home. Many people appreciate having an area outdoors where they can spend leisure time, entertain guests, or throw dinner on the grill.

Some builders may offer premium deck products as optional choices such as LP's WeatherBest® composite decking that looks like wood, but resists rotting, decay, and splintering and never needs staining or painting. While this product's installation has a higher price, the long term costs are very competitive with more traditional materials (see *Product Spotlight*).

Decks are elevated platforms, usually constructed of pressure-treated wood and edged with a railing for safety. Patios, on the other hand, are typically concrete, stone, or brick surfaces positioned directly on the ground.

Landscaping

Landscaping is critical to the aesthetic beauty of both your home and the overall community. The builder and landscaper should take special care in designing the landscape package to fully complement the exterior design of each home.

Once your builder is finished with all the exterior work for your home, the landscaping can be installed without fear of disturbance. Let's get started.

First, to prepare the grounds for landscaping, your builder will have the rough grade performed, which means leveling the ground around the home with bulldozers, tractors, and grading equipment. Then it's time for the final grade to smooth any tire ruts or other imperfections in the yard's surface and assure a smooth lawn—as well as to

A large bulldozer makes sure that the homesite drains properly.

establish the drainage swales and any other desired contours. These drainage swales are critically important. They're part of a system designed to drain excess water from your entire community. DO NOT fill them in, and take care to maintain them, or else you may have a lot of angry neighbors with flooded yards.

Once the rough grade and final grade have been completed, landscaping can begin. A typical landscape planting will include a variety of low-lying shrubs, one or two shade trees, a decorative mulch bed spanning the front of the home, sodded front and side yards, and a seeded back yard. Your builder will have already worked closely with the landscaper to

A smaller finish grader prepares the yard for shrubs, sod and seed.

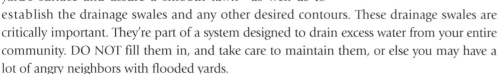

| Start | | Month 2 | Month 3 | Month 4 | Month 5 | Finish |

We add all the little things that make the big things look even better...

The sod can be laid in a few hours but requires days of special attention to make sure that it thrives.

determine the appropriate plantings for that particular region and climate, and the landscape order will have been placed with a nursery several weeks in advance of installation to ensure the availability of the desired shrubs, trees, and sod. Landscaping deliveries are typically made in three phases: trees and shrubs, mulch, and sod or seeding.

Sod is the ideal method for planting grass because the grass is already rooted in its top soil. This instant yard is generally too costly of a method for the entire yard, causing some builders to sod only the front yard. If your builder chooses to plant grass seed instead of laying sod, it's a good idea to use hydro-seeding—an advanced seeding process that is quickly replacing the traditional seed and straw method. The hydro-seeding mixture (a combination of seed, fertilizer, and wood fibers to retain moisture), is blown onto the soil through a large hose. The seed and fertilizer blend is engineered to germinate within two weeks and can very quickly produce a full, healthy lawn.

But not without your care and maintenance! It's your builder's responsibility to "lay the necessary groundwork" and "plant the seeds" for a healthy and attractive yard. Your builder should also provide you with the information you need to properly develop and maintain your yard; for example, you should be informed as to what kinds of trees and shrubs have been installed and how best to care for them.

After that, it's up to you. Ignoring the needs of any lawn will result in something less than a "golf course" appearance. (In fact, if you want your lawn to look like a golf course, you might want to do what country clubs do: hire a superintendent.) Your efforts and the proper applications of water, fertilizer, weed control, and future re-seeding will ultimately determine the

Our Two Cents:

Just because you have freeze-proof spigots doesn't mean you're safe from freezing. You need to make sure your hoses are disconnected from the silcock for the freeze-proof feature of the silcock to work properly. Leaving your hose on the silcock for even one night of below-freezing temperature can burst a pipe, and you'll have a mess on your hands. You may not even find the trouble for weeks or even months. Best advice: take in the hoses in October and wash the car at the car wash for a few months.

appearance of your lawn; for example, grass seed germination under even the best conditions is only 60 to 80 percent, so you'll have to overseed at least once (and probably twice) to ensure a lush, consistent lawn.

Once landscaping, sod or seed, and mulch are in place, your builder will position splash blocks under each gutter downspout to direct rain runoff away from your home and prevent ground erosion. It's wise to use heavy concrete splash blocks that can withstand inevitable abuse from the elements (as well as from your lawnmower).

What if your home is finishing in the winter and there's snow on the ground? It may be necessary for your builder to wait until spring to install the landscaping. If this is the case, your mortgage lender may require your builder to establish an escrow account to hold the funds for landscaping until the time of installation.

Once the landscaping is completed, you'll be able to see how it finishes off a home on the outside. You'll easily imagine future springs and summers full of greenery and flowering plants, as well as endless hours of mowing, trimming, pruning, watering, mulching, pulling weeds... .

Yep, it's work. But it's the only way to have the benefits of a great yard.

Once the plants and mulch are in place, splash blocks are installed to channel water away from the home. This splash block is installed properly, allowing water to overflow as opposed to wash out the end of the block.

Our Two Cents:

You might wonder why your new home comes with some kind of warranty on virtually everything—except landscaping.

The answer is simple. Landscaping requires too much care and maintenance from you, the homeowner, and every homeowner treats his or her yard differently. You might be the type who gets down on your hands and knees and manicures your lawn with cuticle scissors. Then again, you might be the type who cuts the grass every three weeks whether it needs it or not.

Yes, landscape warranties are generally available, and the cost is generally a one-time replacement cost; that is, if your landscaping package cost $1,000, your warranty will also cost $1,000 and will replace everything once. If one of your trees dies, your warranty will replace it. But if you want to cover the new tree, it will cost you whatever the tree costs to replace again.

Our advice: don't bother with the expense of a warranty. Take care of your yard. In the long run, it's the only sensible plan. And know that it's unlikely that *all* of your landscaping will survive. Count on having to replace an element or two.

We add all the little things that make the big things look even better...   125

Appliances are some of the last items installed in a new home for security reasons. Appliances are creature comforts and used daily. Dependable appliances like Maytag come highly recommended. (See Product Spotlight)

FINAL INTERIOR IMPROVEMENTS
Details, Details

Final interior improvements include all items which prepare your home for its ultimate occupants—namely, you and your family. These improvements include final paint touchups, minor repairs, final appliance installation, and a thorough cleaning of the entire home.

Final appliance installation

Although some appliances may have been installed at the time of plumbing or electrical finish, your builder will usually wait until the final locks have been placed on the home before installing major appliances to reduce the risk of theft. Final appliance installation usually includes the range, microwave, refrigerator, washing machine, and dryer, and all of them should be checked to make sure they're running properly after they've been installed. Conscientious builders will include high-quality, name-brand appliances that include detailed manufacturer's warranties. You should check the exact brand and grade of the appliances installed in your new home with what you and your builder agreed upon in your initial meetings.

Quality review and punch list completion

Now it's time for your builder to perform a thorough inspection of the entire home, commonly referred to as "the quality review." During the quality review, your builder will look for any imperfections in the drywall, trim work, painting, flooring, cabinets, and mechanical fixtures.

Repairs and touchups are inevitable because even the best builders and most experienced craftsmen are going to experience some glitches. For instance, it is very common, even expected, for drywall, paint, or finish to need spot attention due to accidental nicks or mars caused by workers.

After going through the home, your builder creates a "punch list" of items that need attention. These items are usually marked in the home in some manner. Different systems exist for each individual builder, but one common procedure is for the builder to place a system of colored stickers on the walls, woodwork, and other areas that need special

attention. Orange stickers may indicate the need for drywall repair, while blue stickers indicate the need for paint touchup, and a green sticker marks the spot where a miscellaneous repair is needed. As repairs and touchups are made, the stickers are removed and the items are rechecked and crossed off the punch list.

Final cleaning

After all the necessary repairs and touchup work have been completed and the traffic flow of workers in and out of the house has subsided, your builder will arrange to have a cleaning team prepare the home for final inspection and home presentation. The cleaning team usually comes two or three times during the final stages of construction so that the home remains clean throughout the final days before closing. The cleaning team typically sweeps the carpet, washes vinyl or tiled surfaces, cleans the windows inside and out, dusts all fixtures and shelves, and maintains the general cleanliness of the entire home. After the final paint touchup, the cleaning crew will remove any protective paper coverings from the carpet, vinyl, or tile, and clean the floorings, baseboards, windows, cabinets, and countertops one final time.

The home is usually cleaned three times during the finishing stages. The final clean is just before the home is presented to the happy homeowners.

The closing process is exciting; however, a great deal of paperwork is involved. Be prepared to sign documents for up to an hour.

☑ HOME PRESENTATION AND CLOSING

Drum Roll, Please...

After the final cleaning, your home should be in its finished condition. Your builder is now ready to present the home to you and get your approval on the quality of workmanship. Because, really, your approval is the approval that matters most.

At the home presentation, your builder will have two objectives while walking through the home with you. First, your builder wants to formally present the home to you so that all the new features, materials, and appliances can be demonstrated and explained in detail. Your builder will also inform you of any particular maintenance requirements for these items.

Second, this is the time for you to inspect the home on the interior and exterior and create another punch list of last-minute items needing attention before the home can be considered complete. Typically, homebuilders have some sort of incentive program which rewards the construction manager for the quality of the finished home based on the number

Residential Warranty Corporation (RWC) • www.rwcwarranty.com

Residential Warranty Corporation is one of the nation's oldest and largest providers of written insured warranties on new homes, providing homeowners with a strong foundation of security for their home. RWC warranties are available only through builders who have met rigorous screening criteria established by the program.

Also, because one warranty rarely meets everyone's needs, RWC has created a menu of warranties and services through a network of affiliated companies. The result is comprehensive coverage and effective risk management for the greatest long-term stability.

Does your builder offer an RWC warranty?

RESIDENTIAL WARRANTY CORPORATION ®
Innovative Leader in Warranty Coverage

---

of items (or lack thereof) on the homeowner's punch list. But that's not your concern. Don't be shy. Speak up. If things need to be corrected, this is your chance.

Final inspection

Before the home is allowed to close, the city building inspectors must return to the site one last time to perform the final inspection. The inspectors check the home to make sure that all mechanical systems are operable and that the home is habitable. If the home passes inspection, a "Certificate of Occupancy" is issued and the home is ready to close.

Closing package

Now that your home is completely finished, it's time for the paperwork. Your builder needs to prepare and assemble a myriad of legal documents to take to the closing. There are literally hundreds of documents associated with the closing package—some required by the mortgage lender, some required by the title company, and others by local government. The preparation of these documents is extremely involved and more than a little time consuming. For this reason, a professional builder who builds many homes a year must have a support staff to assist with the details.

Most builders provide a customer service program, manufacturer's warranties, and a 10-year structural warranty from an insurance company. Residential Warranty Corporation is a very good insurance choice. (See Product Spotlight)

Documents required for closing include the title work, property deed, affidavit, and property survey. The builder's closing coordinator orders the title work, deed, and affidavit from a title company and assembles the documents into one comprehensive package that's taken to the closing. As a convenience for you, your builder may make duplicates of all the documents and assemble them in an organized binder.

Typically, the closing package will include:

- Closing Papers—title, deed, affidavit, neighborhood association information, mortgage survey, and any other information related to the closing.
- Warranties—any manufacturer's warranties and care instructions on materials.
- Service Package—the builder may supply names and telephone numbers of the contractors who can be called upon for emergency home repairs or service.
- Home Warranty—in most states, the homebuilder is obligated, by implied warranty, to guarantee workmanship and materials free from defects for a period of time; however, most municipalities do not mandate builders to provide a written warranty.

At the time of the closing, your builder will review the entire closing package with the new homeowner—yes, that's you. Your builder will answer any final questions you have and present you with the keys to your dream, now a reality: your new home.

Congratulations! Oh, and one last thing…

✖ Hard Hat Area: Watch for falling building standards.

Today in the homebuilding industry, there is a growing movement toward having a quality assurance (QA) person who is not the builder actually take possession of the home and present it to the homeowner. The QA person is expected to be more objective about the flaws that might exist in the home and to dispassionately note problems that need attention. This QA person usually specializes in quality control and customer communications, and may have actually performed some quality inspections during the construction process of your home.

Having specialists on board for the inspections is helpful because they're trained to look for issues that the onsite builder may not notice. While a builder may build 30 to 50 homes (or fewer) a year, the QA person may inspect 200 or more homes.

Homebuilding companies that use only the onsite builder for inspections often have a less-than-thorough QA process; sometimes the builder can be too close to the project, and an outside eye will result in a better, more thorough inspection. Some builders even rely solely on your punch list. Hey—aren't you the least experienced person on the team? That's not right!

A New Beginning (or The Morning After)

The birds are singing. The first rays of the morning sun break the horizon and illuminate your bedroom—your brand-new bedroom in your brand-new home, where you're awakening for the first time. This place that you've been thinking about and agonizing over for so long is now a reality. It has freshly painted walls and shining fixtures. The appliances are all new and the driveway doesn't have a single oil stain on it. Life is good.

A lot of work goes into giving these keys a place to call home.

Of course, your home will not stay new. Walls will get marked by finger-prints and scuffed by furniture movers. Countertops will get scratched. The driveway may start to get a crack or two. The grout in the bathroom may mildew. One afternoon, you may come home to find that Junior has caused the toilet in your master bathroom to overflow. Your electricity may go out just as your favorite team is about to score a game-winning touchdown. You may discover a leak in your roof during the middle of a freezing winter.

Welcome to home ownership.

No, we're not trying to bring you down. Just maybe a little down to earth. Our point is that with a new home comes the responsibility to maintain and care for it.

And relax. All of the things mentioned above can be easily fixed or prevented, if you continue to do your homework.

You are now living in a quality-built home that is the result of months of hard work by experienced and trained craftsmen, thousands of dollars in the best materials and techniques and craftsmanship, and an enormous amount of your own time spent ensuring that quality every step of the way. You've spent an incredible amount of time, energy, and money to make your dream a reality. Now that your dream exists, it only makes sense to do what you can to keep it the beautiful, comfortable, and secure home you knew it would be.

And the best way to keep your house in shape is to have a scheduled routine of maintenance around your home and an understanding of the products and services in your home. Those two things will go a long way toward saving you time and money—not to mention the hassles of dealing with larger problems. So, let's get you started right away. Here are some tips to get your homeownership experience off on the right foot:

- Be sure to read the warranties on the materials, appliances, and products in your home.
- Understand how things work: what you can fix yourself and when you should call for service.
- Know the limitations and properties of countertops, flooring, and appliances, and don't exceed those limitations.
- Schedule the routine checking, cleaning, and parts replacements of products and materials (e.g., cleaning gutters, replacing the furnace filter, polishing fixtures, reinforcing caulk both inside and out, filling small cracks in concrete, changing batteries in smoke alarms, etc.).
- Take the necessary steps to prepare your house for the seasonal changes, making your home comfortable and energy efficient.
- Don't be overly alarmed by the media crisis du jour. While lead paint, radon gas, asbestos, mold, and other problems are great press, they aren't even remotely as common as the media would lead you to believe.

We can't cover everything that you will need to include in your home care routine in this book; that would take a whole 'nother book. But, in general, when you take care of your home, your home will take care of you. While the list of home maintenance tasks may seem a bit overwhelming, you'll soon discover that it's not. It's a practical and essential responsibility of owning your own home.

And don't be afraid to ask your builder any questions you have during the construction process, closing, and after you move in. That's another reason you chose so carefully those many months ago: you want a builder who will continue to be responsive and responsible after the home's completed.

And that's it for us. Buying a new home is probably the single largest and most significant investment you'll make in your lifetime. We hope you've enjoyed this look at what it takes to build your new home. And we hope you've learned something along the way about how to choose the right builder for you.

Now, get going. You're a homeowner. You have stuff you need to do.

CONSTRUCTION KNOWLEDGE QUIZ

Think you're ready to build the home of your dreams? Let's find out! Answer the following questions to test your construction knowledge and see how you measure up. Go ahead and use the book for reference if you want—this is an open-book test! Or just circle the best answer and check your results. Answers begin on Page 139.

1. **What ultimately carries the weight of the home and prevents the home from settling?**
    A. Footings
    B. Slab
    C. Sill plate

2. **What components can be used in building the floor to make it more solid and help eliminate squeaks?**
    A. Headers
    B. Fascias
    C. Bridging or bracing

3. **Interior insulation isn't the only material used to insulate the home. The exterior of the home is insulated with material called:**
    A. Drywall
    B. Sheathing
    C. Siding

4. **What pre-engineered roof system is more costly but generally preferred by most builders?**
    A. Rafters
    B. Trusses
    C. Soffits

5. There are two primary methods of ventilating the attic. Of the two methods, which one provides the best, most complete air circulation?
   A. Continuous soffit and ridge venting
   B. Pod venting

6. Acrylic paint is one of the best paints to use on the exterior of your home because:
   A. It's mold and mildew resistant, holds the color longer, and is very durable.
   B. Once you use it, you'll never have to paint your home again.
   C. It's also the best sealant to use on any exterior home covering.

7. A community with multiple styles of homes, common areas, recreation areas, and more it known as a:
   A. New neighborhood
   B. Master-planned community
   C. Production home community

8. Which of the following serves to fasten the frame of the home to the foundation?
   A. Sill plate
   B. Stake-out
   C. Anchor bolts

9. What does the term "rough-in" mean?
   A. The preliminary installation of the HVAC, plumbing, and electrical systems.
   B. The stage of construction when the rudimentary frame of the home is constructed.
   C. A practice whereby items such as cabinets, doors, and windows are set into position but not fully installed in order to meet deadlines or pass building inspections.

10. Heat pump technology is based on the principle that thermal energy can be extracted from the outside air and brought into the home to provide warmth. When a home is equipped with a heat pump unit, how is the home cooled in the summer months?
    A. A separate air conditioning unit must be installed to cool the home.
    B. The heat pump blower continually circulates air through the home, creating a cooling sensation, much like a window fan.
    C. The heat pump reverses its cycle, sending the extracted heat outside and keeping the cool air inside the home.

11. Which of the following terms refers to the stage of construction where the home is near completion and the builder inspects the home for any final details to be addressed?
    A. Final grade
    B. Quality review
    C. Home presentation

12. If you're driving down an interstate and you see a home drive by, the home is:
    A. Speeding.
    B. A manufactured or modular home.
    C. A figment of your imagination.

13. A slab foundation, basement walls, driveways, and sidewalks are all composed of poured concrete. Any cracks forming in the surface of these elements should be corrected immediately after formation, before construction proceeds and damage is done to the permanent structure.
    A. True
    B. False

14. What does the term "R-value" refer to?
    A. The electrical resistance property of a specific gauge of wire.
    B. The ability of a roofing shingle to reflect sunlight and heat.
    C. The ability of an insulation material to resist the passage of heat.

15. **Which of the following is the means for distributing water inside the home to the plumbing fixtures?**
    A. Water main
    B. Water lateral
    C. Water supply lines

16. **What does the term "drywall" refer to?**
    A. Panels of gypsum board which are affixed to the frame of a home, effectively creating the walls and ceilings.
    B. A waterproofing system used on the exterior of a home's basement walls consisting of a rubberized spray-on coating and panels of fiberboard which allow for water runoff.
    C. A plaster-based putty which is applied over sections of wood lath to form the walls and ceilings of a home.

17. **Which of the following is the ideal method for planting grass on a yard?**
    A. Hydro-seeding
    B. Sod
    C. Straw-and-seed

18. **Hardiplank® is a:**
    A. Sailing term.
    B. Something one carpenter says to another carpenter when there's a loud noise.
    C. A fiber-reinforced cement sheet horizontal siding.

19. **Which of the following documents contains the information and measurements identifying the exact physical placement of the home on the homesite?**
    A. Building permit
    B. Blueprint
    C. Plot plan

20. **The term HVAC is an acronym for heating, ventilation, and air conditioning. The HVAC system serves the purpose of distributing the 'conditioned' (heated or cooled) air throughout the home.**
    A. True
    B. False

21. **To find a quality builder for your new home, you should:**
    A. Place an ad in the newspaper.
    B. Consult an astrologer.
    C. Talk with homeowners, real estate professionals, and the local builders association.

22. **Which type of homebuilder builds the largest number of homes in today's market?**
    A. Scattered lot builder
    B. Custom builder
    C. Semi-custom builder
    D. Production builder

23. **Which of the following is generally regarded as the preferred method of frame construction?**
    A. Stick-built construction
    B. Panelized construction
    C. Lincoln Logs and wire

24. **If you see a broken window in your new home during the construction process, you should:**
    A. Call your builder every day until it's fixed.
    B. Ignore it.
    C. Call, then give your builder time to fix it.

25. **The only thing more fun than building a new home is:**
    A. Writing about it.
    B. Tearing it down.
    C. Living in it.

CONSTRUCTION KNOWLEDGE
QUIZ ANSWERS

1. **A. Footings**

   The footings are the trenched areas that are filled with high-compression concrete and serve as the base on which the slab, crawlspace, or basement walls rest. *(See Footings, Chapter 5, Page 37)*

2. **C. Bridging or bracing**

   Cross-bracing of floor joists, called bridging, eliminates independent movement of the joists and the bouncy "trampoline" effect found in homes without bridging. Bridging also helps prevent the floor from squeaking. *(See Floor Systems, Chapter 6, Page 56)*

3. **B. Sheathing**

   The sheathing both reinforces the wall and provides an initial layer of insulation for the home. Sheathing is attached to the exterior walls of the frame using a collared, or capped, nail. *(See Sheathing, Chapter 6, Page 62.)*

4. **B. Trusses**

   Trusses are large triangular frame pieces that form the roof. Because trusses are engineered for maximum strength and manufactured offsite to ensure precision, they can be more cost effective. However, it is typically accepted that trusses provide a much more reliable roof system. *(See Roof Systems, Chapter 6, Page 63.)*

5. **A. Continuous soffit and ridge venting**

   Ridge venting allows more hot air to ventilate out of the attic space. Continuous soffit venting allows more ventilation than traditional ventilation because it spans the length of the soffit. Though more expensive than traditional pod and soffit venting, homes with ridge and continuous soffit venting usually require less air conditioning in the summer. Because of cooler temperatures on the surface of the roof, this type of venting also extends the life of the shingles and other roofing materials. *(see Roofing: Attic Vents, Chapter 6, Page 71, and Exterior Trim, Chapter 6, Page 72.)*

6. **A. It's mold and mildew resistant, holds the color longer, and is very durable.**
   Which means it will keep your new home looking great longer. *(See Exterior Painting, Chapter 6, Page 74.)*

7. **B. Master-planned community**
   A master-planned community typically has homes in a variety of different price points and all sorts of shared community amenities. It's almost as if, instead of creating a new neighborhood or subdivision, the builder is creating a new town, with homes ideal for young families, singles, couples, empty nesters, large families, and others. *(See Master-Planned Communities, Chapter 3, Page 25.)*

8. **C. Anchor bolts**
   Anchor bolts are large metal bolts that protrude upward from the foundation wall and fit though drilled holes in the sill plate of the wall frames. Once the walls are in position, washers and nuts are attached to the anchor bolts, effectively fastening the frame to the foundation. *(See Slab Foundation, Chapter 5, Page 40.)*

9. **A. The preliminary installation of the mechanical systems**
   "Rough-in" is a generic term builders use to refer to the stage of construction where the preliminary provisions are made for the mechanical systems. For example, during the HVAC rough-in, the network of metal ducts and vents is put into position in the wall, ceilings, and floors. *(See Chapter 7, Page 81.)*

10. **C. The heat pump reverses its cycle, sending the extracted heat outside and keeping the cool air inside the home.**
    A heat pump is a reversible unit that individually performs the dual function of heating the home in the winter months and cooling the home in the summer months. The basic concept is that the heat pump is capable of extracting thermal energy (heat) from the outside air. To heat the home, that thermal energy is brought inside. To cool the home, the heat pump does the opposite: it extracts heat inside and sends it outside while dispersing the remaining cool throughout the inside of the home. *(See Heat Pumps, Chapter 7, Page 84.)*

11. **B. Quality review**

When the home is near completion, the builder will perform the quality review, at which time the builder carefully inspects the entire home to assure that all work has been performed satisfactorily. The builder will generally create a "punch list" of items that need attention before the home can be presented to the homeowner. *(See Quality Review, Chapter 9, Page 126.)*

12. **B. A manufactured or modular home**

This type of home is made in factories and shipped as house sections complete with electrical, plumbing, cabinets, and even carpeting already installed. *(See Types of Construction, Chapter 2, Page 14.)*

13. **False**

It's very common for small cracks to form in the surface of concrete. This is a natural part of the curing process for concrete and should be expected. However, if surface cracks should widen to about the width of a nickel, then the builder may want to consider repairing or replacing that section of concrete, depending on its location. *(See Pouring the Slab, Chapter 5, Page 43.)*

14. **C. The ability of an insulation material to resist the passage of heat.**

All insulation materials are typically given an "R-value" rating, and the builder needs to be aware of these ratings so that the appropriate level of insulation can be achieved for each wall and ceiling. *(See Insulation, Chapter 7, Page 92.)*

15. **C. Water supply lines**

The water supply line network is the means of distributing the fresh water throughout the home to the actual plumbing fixtures. The water service line is the pipeline that transports the water from the water main (located near the street), through the water meter (located in the water pit, typically in the front yard, and into the home. *(See Plumbing Systems, Chapter 7, Page 86.)*

16. **A. Panels of gypsum board which are affixed to the frame of a home, effectively creating the walls and ceilings.**

The drywall forms the smooth, finished surface of a wall and ceiling and effectively covers the raw frames and preliminary mechanical work. *(See Drywall, Chapter 8, Page 99.)*

17. B. Sod

Covering a yard with sod is the ideal method for planting grass because the seed has already taken root in its top soil and provides an instant cover of grass. However, the hydro-seeding process provides an excellent, affordable alternative to sod. Many builders are using a combination of sod and hydro-seed to cover a home's yard; for the most part, the traditional straw-and-seed technique has been left by the wayside. *(See Landscaping, Chapter 9, Page 123.)*

18. C. Fiber-reinforced cement sheet vertical siding.

Hardiplank® is a new, durable alternative to cedar and other wood sidings. It has the look and warmth of wood, but is resistant to many of the wood's enemies: rot, termites, water damage, and U-V rays. *(See Siding, Chapter 6, Page 73.)*

19. C. Plot plan

The plot plan is a technical drawing created by an engineer that details the precise measurements and layout of the home in relation to property boundaries, public easements, water and sewer lines, etc. that might affect where the home can be positioned on the site. *(See Plot Plans, Chapter 4, Page 29.)*

20. True

The HVAC system does, in fact, distribute the conditioned air throughout the home. It also returns air back to the heat pump or other heating or cooling unit. An HVAC is an input/output system. *(See HVAC Systems, Chapter 7, Page 82.)*

21. C. Talk with homeowners, real estate professionals, and the local builders association.

Asking questions and talking with the people who can give you answers is the best way to find a reputable builder for your home. The final product, your new home, will be the result of the quality of builder you select. Do your homework early and make a well-informed decision. *(See Chapter 3, Page 19.)*

22. D. Production builder

Since 1975, the number of residential homes built by production builders in the United States has increased tremendously. Today, the number of homes built by production builders far outnumbers those build by other types of builders and has equaled the quality and diversity of designs available. *(See Homebuilding Trends, Chapter 1, Page 3.)*

23. **A. Stick-built construction**

The most preferred method of construction is stick-built construction. With stick-built construction, raw materials—in particular, the lumber for the frame—are delivered to the jobsite, where the lumber is measured, cut, and assembled board by board, according to the specifications of each individual floor plan *(see Types of Construction, Chapter 2, Page 16.)*

24. **C. Call, then give your builder time to fix it.**

Damage to your home during construction is inevitable. But your builder knows about these things, and things take time to fix. Remember, your builder is working on a master schedule. It might take a couple of weeks to get a new window ordered and delivered. So if you see a broken window and tell your builder about it, be patient. The damage will be corrected. *(See Our Two Cents, Chapter 5, Page 53.)*

25. **C. Living in it**

Sure, writing about it was fun. But nothing beats living in your new home. You picked the floor plan, the site, the design, and the builder you wanted for your new home. Enjoy it!

How'd you score? Are you ready to build or do you need a refresher course?

# Correct	Your Rank
25-22	Master Builder
21-18	Journeyman
17-14	Apprentice
13-0	Thumb-smasher